Healing with Ki-Kou

Ki-Kou

The Secrets of Ancient Chinese Breathing Techniques

ISBN 0-9581576-3-4

Translated from the original book published by Houken Publishing
(The Socio Health Group)1993.

Contents

About the Author

Dr. Li Xiuling was born in Beijing, China, in 1949. Her parents, grandparents, and ancestors were traditional Chinese doctors, and the family home has been used for Chinese medicine for the last 800 years.

Starting as a child, Dr. Li was educated by her family in Chinese herbal medicine, Chinese medicine, and *chi*, the vital energy force of all life.

At the age of 18, she opened a Chinese medical clinic, and educated and trained 12 Chinese doctors. After that, she entered Beijing Medical University to learn Western medicine. After graduating from Beijing Medical University, she studied at the Institute of Chinese Traditional Medicine, while working at an elite medical center in Beijing.

She also studied at the Nippon Medical School, in a program to combine Eastern medicine with more scientifically based Western methods. She is presently a member of the Japan Eastern Medical Organization.

Today, Dr. Li studies neurology at Tokyo Women's Medical College and is a lecturer in the Department of Neurology, the First Hospital, Beijing Medical University. She recently recorded—for the first time known—the system of secret Chinese breathing techniques known as Ki-kou, a system handed down from generation to generation of Chinese healers.

Acknowledgments

Many people contributed to the publishing of this book. The publisher wishes to thank Joe Wayno of Houken Publishing, SocioHealth division, for bringing *Healing with Ki-Kou* to Agora Health Books and working with us every step of the way. Thanks also to Taka Hirayama, who translated the manuscript, Judith Strauss for editing the book, and Ken Danz for copyediting and proofing the final product. EVS Communications typeset and designed the text, and Christie Santiago of Agora Publishing designed the cover.

Introduction

Though virtually unknown in this country, the healing Chinese breathing techniques that I am introducing in this book—*Ki-kou*—are easy to understand and easy to follow. If you practice them every day, you will not only become aware of the powerful connection between your mind and your body but also improve your overall health, well-being, and quality of life.

Before you begin, understand that you must keep an open mind. To successfully use these exercises to prevent and treat disease, you must believe that they will work. Positive thinking will help you get in touch with your inner self, and only then will you be able to unlock your own natural healing abilities.

How *Ki-kou* Works

Ki-kou teaches you how to relax your mind and body. As you relax, you will feel yourself become calmer and calmer. When you are completely at peace, healing energy (what the Chinese call *chi*) will be able to flow freely throughout your body.

The healthy body is one that is in balance and has a strong flow of *chi*. If your *chi* is blocked, that part of your body loses balance and becomes ill. When you practice *Ki-kou* on a regular basis, you use specific exercises to guide your *chi* through these obstructions and help your body heal itself.

It cannot be seen or touched, but every living creature has *chi*. To the Chinese, it does not need to be explained or demonstrated — it is a part of their being. Once you start to practice *Ki-kou*, you, too, will recognize the existence of *chi* within you.

Three Important Steps Before You Begin

1. **Make yourself as comfortable as possible.**
Wear loose clothing and take off your shoes,
your watch, and so on. Release your tension and
stress by closing your eyes halfway and relaxing
your muscles, your joints—your entire body. (To
relax your facial muscles, it helps to smile.)

We call the *Ki-kou* postures "conditioning your
body," or *chou-shin*. The specific postures you
will be assuming depend on which exercises you
will be doing. Just remember that no matter what
position you are in, you should never feel any
discomfort.

2. **Clear your mind.** As you feel your body
becoming calmer and calmer, gradually let go of
your thoughts and start to focus on achieving
complete mental and physical relaxation—what
we call "balancing your mind" or *chou-shin*. At

Notes
- Do not try to practice *Ki-kou* on a full
  stomach or if you have been drinking
  alcohol.
- The best place to practice *Ki-kou* is
  outdoors, surrounded by nature. If that's
  not possible, use a quiet, dimly lit room
  in your home.
- Before you begin, refresh yourself by
  rinsing your mouth with water.

this point, you will be ready to use specific *Ki-kou* exercises to heal the parts of your body that need treatment. Don't allow any disturbing thoughts to intrude and disrupt this peaceful state.

3. **Concentrate on your breathing.** Breathing is a very important element of *Ki-kou*, and there are several effective methods that can be used. The basic technique is to inhale deeply through your nose and exhale slowly through your mouth. Use this technique unless the instructions for a particular exercise specify otherwise. No matter what method you use, don't force it. Your breathing should be calm, deep, slow, and rhythmic—and as relaxed as your body and mind are. This is what we call "balancing breathing," or *chou-soku*.

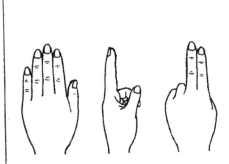

Notes

- All of the Chinese words in this book — including the names of the individual exercises that are prescribed for various conditions — are written phonetically, to give you an idea of the way the original Chinese characters are pronounced. Because of the complexity of the Chinese language, some words may sound the same even though they have different meanings.
- The numbers on the illustrations correspond to the numbered instructions for each exercise.
- The pressure points in your body that are stimulated by certain exercises are shown along with those exercises. In Chinese, the position of each pressure point is indicated by what we call "finger-measuring," or *shiryou-hou*. However, I have used terms that you are more familiar with to try to describe exactly where these pressure points are located.

Chi-shi and *Shu-kon*:
The *Ki-kou* Pre- and Post-Workout Exercises

Every *Ki-kou* workout begins with *chi-shi*, the following warm-up exercise:

1. *Be-mu*: Stand up, sit on a chair, or sit cross-legged on the floor with your eyes closed.
2. *Chang-tsuo*: Calm your mind.
3. *Tsuo-shou*: Put your palms together and rub them up and down until they feel warm.

4. *Bou-chee*: With your hands spread apart as if you were holding a big ball in front of you, inhale through your nose. Exhale through your mouth while bringing your hands back together.

Every *Ki-kou* workout ends with *shu-kon*, the following cool-down exercise:

1. *Ko-chi*: Make a chewing motion with your mouth five to 100 times.

2. *Tu-na*: Sit on a chair or sit cross-legged on the floor with your eyes closed. Calm your mind. Inhale through your nose and hold your breath for two seconds. While you are holding your breath, imagine that *chi* is flowing from your brain and down your spinal cord and lower back. Exhale slowly through your mouth. When you breathe out, imagine that you are releasing the old *chi* from your body. When you breathe in, imagine that you are inhaling fresh *chi* from nature.

Using *Ki-Kou* breathing to draw healing *chi* through your body

Inhale slowly, picturing yourself drawing in the *chi* in the air. While you are inhaling, imagine that you are pulling the *chi* through your body, following the path indicated by the arrows in the diagram below. With practice, you will be able to pull the *chi* through your entire body in one breath. How long should each *Ki-kou* breathing session be? That depends on how sick you are and what you are trying to accomplish. In general, if you are using *Ki-kou* breathing for healing, it should be done for approximately 30 minutes at a time.

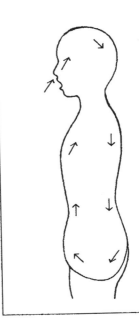

- *In-dou* is the pressure point between your eyebrows.
- *Tai-you* are the pressure points between the outer corners of your eyes and your temples.
- *Hin-sha are* the pressure points found in the hollows made by your jaw when you open your mouth.

3. *Su-wien*: Wipe the inside of your mouth with your tongue three times. Keeping your tongue behind your upper front teeth, inhale through your mouth. Close your lips and move the air around with your lips and cheeks as if you were cleaning your mouth with it. Do this five to 10 times. If saliva begins to collect in your mouth while you are doing this, swallow it.

4. *Shi-yen*: As you inhale, put your index fingers on the *in-dou* pressure point and massage along your eyebrows until you reach the *tai-you* pressure points. Continue massaging your face until you reach the *hin-sha* pressure points and then massage your neck and chest as shown in the illustration. Repeat three times.

5. *Shu-to*: Close your eyes and put your index fingers on the *in-dou* pressure point. Massage your forehead and your scalp, moving down the back of your head, down your neck, and across your shoulders as shown in the illustration. Repeat three times.

6. *Shun-yo*: Sit on a chair and lift both of your arms up, back, and over your head with your wrists bent. Lift your feet off the floor and bend your toes. Inhale slowly and stretch your back. Then exhale while you bring your arms down to your sides and relax your entire body. Repeat twice.

Specific Breathing Techniques to Prevent and Treat Liver and Digestive-System Disorders

For Chronic Gastritis: *Shin-chen-chi-ju*

1. Sitting on a chair or cross-legged on the floor, warm up with *chi-shi*.

2. Place your right hand over your liver and your left hand over your spleen. As you inhale, move your hands from your lower abdomen to your lower back, as illustrated.

Warm up with *chi-shi*

1. *Be-mu*: Stand up, sit on a chair, or sit cross-legged on the floor with your eyes closed.
2. *Chang-tsuo*: Calm your mind.
3. *Tsuo-shou*: Put your palms together and rub them up and down until they feel warm.

4. *Bou-chee*: With your hands spread apart as if you were holding a big ball in front of you, inhale through your nose. Exhale through your mouth while bringing your hands back together.

3. As you exhale, use the back of your hands to move from your lower back to the sides of your lower abdomen. Repeat for five to 10 minutes.
4. Cool down with *shu-kon*.

Cool down with *shu-kon*

1. *Ko-chi*: Make a chewing motion with your mouth five to 100 times.
2. *Tu-na*: Sit on a chair or sit cross-legged on the floor with your eyes closed. Calm your mind. Inhale through your nose and hold your breath for two seconds. While you are holding your breath, imagine that *chi* is flowing from your brain and down your spinal cord and lower back. Exhale slowly through your mouth. When you breathe out, imagine that you are releasing the old *chi* from your body. When you breathe in, imagine that you are inhaling fresh *chi* from nature.

3. *Su-wien*: Wipe the inside of your mouth with your tongue three times. Keeping your tongue behind your upper front teeth, inhale through your mouth. Close your lips and move the air around with your lips and cheeks as if you were cleaning your mouth with it. Do this five to 10 times. If saliva begins to collect in your mouth while you are doing this, swallow it.
4. *Shi-yen*: As you inhale, put your index fingers on the *in-dou* pressure point and massage along your eyebrows until you reach the *tai-you* pressure points. Continue massaging your face until you reach the *hin-sha* pressure points and then massage your neck and chest as shown in the illustration. Repeat three times.

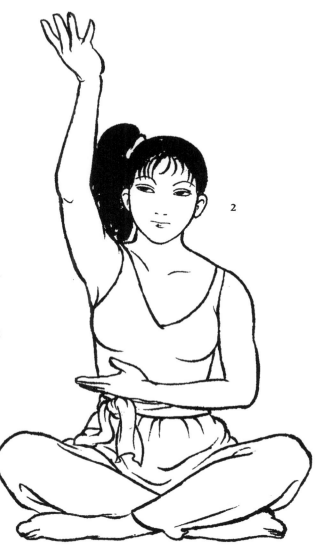

For Gastric and Duodenal Ulcers: *Gu-yu-zo-guon*

1. Sitting cross-legged on the floor, warm up with *chi-shi*.
2. As you inhale through your nose, reach your right hand over your head is if you were trying to pick an apple from a tree. Place your left hand under your right breast with the palm facing up.
3. As you exhale through your mouth, move your right hand under your left breast and reach your left hand over your head.
4. Repeat steps 2 and 3 from 30 to 50 times.
5. Cool down with *shu-kon*.

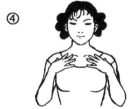

5. *Shu-to*: Close your eyes and put your index fingers on the *in-dou* pressure point. Massage your forehead and your scalp, moving down the back of your head, down your neck, and across your shoulders as shown in the illustration. Repeat three times.

6. *Shun-yo*: Sit on a chair and lift both of your arms up, back, and over your head with your wrists bent. Lift your feet off the floor and bend your toes. Inhale slowly and stretch your back. Then exhale while you bring your arms down to your sides and relax your entire body. Repeat twice.

For Internal Organ Shifting: *Ba-fang-dg-pei*

1. In the cross-legged position, warm up with *chi-shi*.

Warm up with *chi-shi*

1. *Be-mu*: Stand up, sit on a chair, or sit cross-legged on the floor with your eyes closed.
2. *Chang-tsuo*: Calm your mind.
3. *Tsuo-shou*: Put your palms together and rub them up and down until they feel warm.

4. *Bou-chee*: With your hands spread apart as if you were holding a big ball in front of you, inhale through your nose. Exhale through your mouth while bringing your hands back together.

2. Place your left hand on your left knee. Bring your right hand up over your head as if you were holding a small cup in your hand. Inhaling deeply, reach as high as you possibly can, imagining that you are trying to fill your cup with air. As you exhale, bring your right hand back down.
3. Repeat 12 times with your right arm and 12 times with your left arm.
4. Cool down with *shu-kon*.

Cool down with *shu-kon*

1. *Ko-chi*: Make a chewing motion with your mouth five to 100 times.
2. *Tu-na*: Sit on a chair or sit cross-legged on the floor with your eyes closed. Calm your mind. Inhale through your nose and hold your breath for two seconds. While you are holding your breath, imagine that *chi* is flowing from your brain and down your spinal cord and lower back. Exhale slowly through your mouth. When you breathe out, imagine that you are releasing the old *chi* from your body. When you breathe in, imagine that you are inhaling fresh *chi* from nature.

3. *Su-wien*: Wipe the inside of your mouth with your tongue three times. Keeping your tongue behind your upper front teeth, inhale through your mouth. Close your lips and move the air around with your lips and cheeks as if you were cleaning your mouth with it. Do this five to 10 times. If saliva begins to collect in your mouth while you are doing this, swallow it.
4. *Shi-yen*: As you inhale, put your index fingers on the *in-dou* pressure point and massage along your eyebrows until you reach the *tai-you* pressure points. Continue massaging your face until you reach the *hin-sha* pressure points and then massage your neck and chest as shown in the illustration. Repeat three times.

Hepatitis

1. For Bloating, Loss of Appetite, and Jaundice: *Gu-shen-wo-inn*

1. In the cross-legged position, warm up with *chi-shi*.
2. Lie down on the floor as illustrated, with your right arm under your head. Bend your right knee and extend your left leg.
3. With your left hand, massage around the *ki-kai* pressure point as if you were drawing a figure-eight on your stomach. As you massage, breathe deeply 12 to 50 times.
4. Cool down with *shu-kon*.

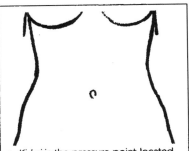

- *Ki-kai* is the pressure point located approximately one inch below your navel.

2, 3

5. *Shu-to*: Close your eyes and put your index fingers on the *in-dou* pressure point. Massage your forehead and your scalp, moving down the back of your head, down your neck, and across your shoulders as shown in the illustration. Repeat three times.

6. *Shun-yo*: Sit on a chair and lift both of your arms up, back, and over your head with your wrists bent. Lift your feet off the floor and bend your toes. Inhale slowly and stretch your back. Then exhale while you bring your arms down to your sides and relax your entire body. Repeat twice.

2. For Fatigue, Bloating and Gas Associated With Hepatitis: *To-teien-dao-jang*

1. In the standing position, warm up with *chi-shi*.

2. Hold your hands in front of your eyes and move them in a circle, clockwise, to draw *chi* into your eyes. Then move your hands to your stomach to draw the *chi* there.

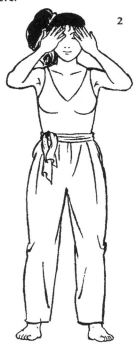

Warm up with *chi-shi*

1. *Be-mu*: Stand up, sit on a chair, or sit cross-legged on the floor with your eyes closed.
2. *Chang-tsuo*: Calm your mind.
3. *Tsuo-shou*: Put your palms together and rub them up and down until they feel warm.

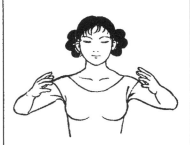

4. *Bou-chee*: With your hands spread apart as if you were holding a big ball in front of you, inhale through your nose. Exhale through your mouth while bringing your hands back together.

Cool down with *shu-kon*

1. *Ko-chi*: Make a chewing motion with your mouth five to 100 times.
2. *Tu-na*: Sit on a chair or sit cross-legged on the floor with your eyes closed. Calm your mind. Inhale through your nose and hold your breath for two seconds. While you are holding your breath, imagine that *chi* is flowing from your brain and down your spinal cord and lower back. Exhale slowly through your mouth. When you breathe out, imagine that you are releasing the old *chi* from your body. When you breathe in, imagine that you are inhaling fresh *chi* from nature.

3. *Su-wien*: Wipe the inside of your mouth with your tongue three times. Keeping your tongue behind your upper front teeth, inhale through your mouth. Close your lips and move the air around with your lips and cheeks as if you were cleaning your mouth with it. Do this five to 10 times. If saliva begins to collect in your mouth while you are doing this, swallow it.
4. *Shi-yen*: As you inhale, put your index fingers on the *in-dou* pressure point and massage along your eyebrows until you reach the *tai-you* pressure points. Continue massaging your face until you reach the *hin-sha* pressure points and then massage your neck and chest as shown in the illustration. Repeat three times.

3. Move your left leg forward. As you inhale, raise your hands (palms up) high over your head and imagine that you are releasing the *chi* on your palms into the air.

4. As you exhale, bring your palms down toward your stomach, imagining that you are drawing new *chi* into your body.

5. Move your right leg forward and repeat step 3.

6. Repeat steps 3 through 5 slowly and rhythmically, taking nine steps forward with each leg.

7. Cool down with *shu-kon*.

4

5

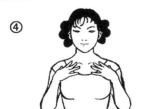

④

⑤

⑥

5. *Shu-to:* Close your eyes and put your index fingers on the *in-dou* pressure point. Massage your forehead and your scalp, moving down the back of your head, down your neck, and across your shoulders as shown in the illustration. Repeat three times.

6. *Shun-yo:* Sit on a chair and lift both of your arms up, back, and over your head with your wrists bent. Lift your feet off the floor and bend your toes. Inhale slowly and stretch your back. Then exhale while you bring your arms down to your sides and relax your entire body. Repeat twice.

3. For Prevention and Treatment of Hepatitis: *Ree-jun-chin*

1. In the cross-legged position, warm up with *chi-shi*.

2. Slowly close your eyes and breathe naturally. Rub your knees with your hands 30 to 50 times, imagining that *chi* is flowing through your entire body.
3. Cool down with *shu-kon*.

Warm up with *chi-shi*

1. *Be-mu*: Stand up, sit on a chair, or sit cross-legged on the floor with your eyes closed.
2. *Chang-tsuo*: Calm your mind.
3. *Tsuo-shou*: Put your palms together and rub them up and down until they feel warm.

4. *Bou-chee*: With your hands spread apart as if you were holding a big ball in front of you, inhale through your nose. Exhale through your mouth while bringing your hands back together.

Cool down with *shu-kon*

1. *Ko-chi*: Make a chewing motion with your mouth five to 100 times.
2. *Tu-na*: Sit on a chair or sit cross-legged on the floor with your eyes closed. Calm your mind. Inhale through your nose and hold your breath for two seconds. While you are holding your breath, imagine that *chi* is flowing from your brain and down your spinal cord and lower back. Exhale slowly through your mouth. When you breathe out, imagine that you are releasing the old *chi* from your body. When you breathe in, imagine that you are inhaling fresh *chi* from nature.

3. *Su-wien*: Wipe the inside of your mouth with your tongue three times. Keeping your tongue behind your upper front teeth, inhale through your mouth. Close your lips and move the air around with your lips and cheeks as if you were cleaning your mouth with it. Do this five to 10 times. If saliva begins to collect in your mouth while you are doing this, swallow it.
4. *Shi-yen*: As you inhale, put your index fingers on the *in-dou* pressure point and massage along your eyebrows until you reach the *tai-you* pressure points. Continue massaging your face until you reach the *hin-sha* pressure points and then massage your neck and chest as shown in the illustration. Repeat three times.

For Loss of Appetite: *Tia-chee-fa*

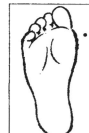

• *Yu-sen* is the pressure point a little above the center of the sole of your foot. If you bend your toes, you will see the hollow that forms around it.

1. In the sitting position, warm up with *chi-shi*.
2. Place both of your hands on your right knee. While exhaling, move them down your shin bone. Repeat 20 times.
3. Pull up your right foot with your hands and press the *yu-sen* pressure point with two fingers, as illustrated. If you extend your right knee a little, you will be able to apply even more pressure. Breathing deeply while moving your right leg up and down, repeat twice.
4. Repeat with your left leg.
5. Cool down with *shun-yo* (step 6—the full-body stretch—of *shu-kon).*

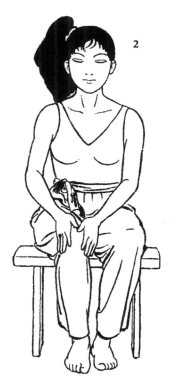

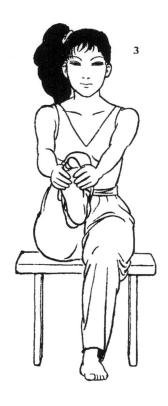

5. *Shu-to:* Close your eyes and put your index fingers on the *in-dou* pressure point. Massage your forehead and your scalp, moving down the back of your head, down your neck, and across your shoulders as shown in the illustration. Repeat three times.

6. *Shun-yo:* Sit on a chair and lift both of your arms up, back, and over your head with your wrists bent. Lift your feet off the floor and bend your toes. Inhale slowly and stretch your back. Then exhale while you bring your arms down to your sides and relax your entire body. Repeat twice.

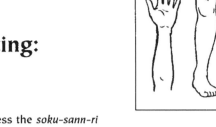

- *Soku-sann-ri is* the pressure point located on the outer side of your shin bone, 1 to 1 ½ inches below your knee.
- *Nai-kan* is the pressure point located on the inside of your arm, approximately one inch above your wrist.

For Nausea and Vomiting:
Zu-shin-chen-ree

1. In the sitting position, warm up with *chi-shi*.

Warm up with *chi-shi*

1. *Be-mu*: Stand up, sit on a chair, or sit cross-legged on the floor with your eyes closed.
2. *Chang-tsuo*: Calm your mind.
3. *Tsuo-shou*: Put your palms together and rub them up and down until they feel warm.

4. *Bou-chee*: With your hands spread apart as if you were holding a big ball in front of you, inhale through your nose. Exhale through your mouth while bringing your hands back together.

2. Press the *soku-sann-ri* pressure point on your left leg with your right heel. As you press down, inhale deeply through your nose. As you release the pressure, exhale very gently. At the same time, press the *nai-kan* pressure point on your left hand with your right thumb. Do the same thing on the other side, applying pressure with your left heel on your right leg and your left thumb on your right hand.
3. Repeat 24 times.
4. Cool down with *shu-kon*.

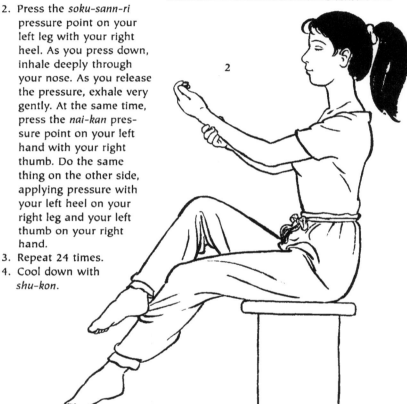

2

Cool down with *shu-kon*

1. *Ko-chi*: Make a chewing motion with your mouth five to 100 times.
2. *Tu-na*: Sit on a chair or sit cross-legged on the floor with your eyes closed. Calm your mind. Inhale through your nose and hold your breath for two seconds. While you are holding your breath, imagine that *chi* is flowing from your brain and down your spinal cord and lower back. Exhale slowly through your mouth. When you breathe out, imagine that you are releasing the old *chi* from your body. When you breathe in, imagine that you are inhaling fresh *chi* from nature.

3. *Su-wien*: Wipe the inside of your mouth with your tongue three times. Keeping your tongue behind your upper front teeth, inhale through your mouth. Close your lips and move the air around with your lips and cheeks as if you were cleaning your mouth with it. Do this five to 10 times. If saliva begins to collect in your mouth while you are doing this, swallow it.
4. *Shi-yen*: As you inhale, put your index fingers on the *in-dou* pressure point and massage along your eyebrows until you reach the *tai-you* pressure points. Continue massaging your face until you reach the *hin-sha* pressure points and then massage your neck and chest as shown in the illustration. Repeat three times.

For Constipation:
Fang-jang-jao-hi

1. Lying on your back, warm up with *chi-shi*.
2. Exhaling deeply, move your hands from your chest to your stomach. Inhaling deeply, move your hands from your stomach to your chest. Repeat six times.
3. Cool down with *shu-kon*.

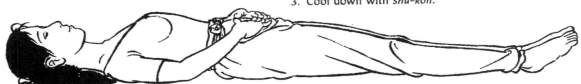

2

For Diarrhea:
Mo-on-fu-shee-wui

1. In the standing position, warm up with *chi-shi*.
2. Gradually open your hands and spread them apart. Step forward on your left leg and bend your knee up and down. Inhale deeply through your nose and exhale slowly through your mouth. With your body relaxed, repeat this movement six to 12 times.
3. Do the same thing with your right leg in the forward position.
4. Cool down with *shu-kon*.

2

④ ⑤ ⑥

5. *Shu-to*: Close your eyes and put your index fingers on the *in-dou* pressure point. Massage your forehead and your scalp, moving down the back of your head, down your neck, and across your shoulders as shown in the illustration. Repeat three times.

6. *Shun-yo*: Sit on a chair and lift both of your arms up, back, and over your head with your wrists bent. Lift your feet off the floor and bend your toes. Inhale slowly and stretch your back. Then exhale while you bring your arms down to your sides and relax your entire body. Repeat twice.

Hemorrhoids

1. For Internal Hemorrhoids: *Shin-shien-chin-ree*

1. In the sitting position, warm up with *chi-shi*.

Warm up with *chi-shi*

1. *Be-mu*: Stand up, sit on a chair, or sit cross-legged on the floor with your eyes closed.
2. *Chang-tsuo*: Calm your mind.
3. *Tsuo-shou*: Put your palms together and rub them up and down until they feel warm.

4. *Bou-chee*: With your hands spread apart as if you were holding a big ball in front of you, inhale through your nose. Exhale through your mouth while bringing your hands back together.

3

2. Bring your right leg up onto the chair with your knee bent, as illustrated.
3. With your fingers touching, move both of your arms above your right knee while breathing deeply. As you inhale, raise your hands upward; as you exhale, bring your hands down. Repeat 12 to 24 times.
4. Switch legs and do the same thing.
5. Cool down with *shu-kon*.

Cool down with *shu-kon*

1. *Ko-chi*: Make a chewing motion with your mouth five to 100 times.
2. *Tu-na*: Sit on a chair or sit cross-legged on the floor with your eyes closed. Calm your mind. Inhale through your nose and hold your breath for two seconds. While you are holding your breath, imagine that *chi* is flowing from your brain and down your spinal cord and lower back. Exhale slowly through your mouth. When you breathe out, imagine that you are releasing the old *chi* from your body. When you breathe in, imagine that you are inhaling fresh *chi* from nature.

3. *Su-wien*: Wipe the inside of your mouth with your tongue three times. Keeping your tongue behind your upper front teeth, inhale through your mouth. Close your lips and move the air around with your lips and cheeks as if you were cleaning your mouth with it. Do this five to 10 times. If saliva begins to collect in your mouth while you are doing this, swallow it.
4. *Shi-yen*: As you inhale, put your index fingers on the *in-dou* pressure point and massage along your eyebrows until you reach the *tai-you* pressure points. Continue massaging your face until you reach the *hin-sha* pressure points and then massage your neck and chest as shown in the illustration. Repeat three times.

2. For External Hemorrhoids or a Combination of Internal and External Hemorrhoids: *Shei-shi-en-chin-ra*

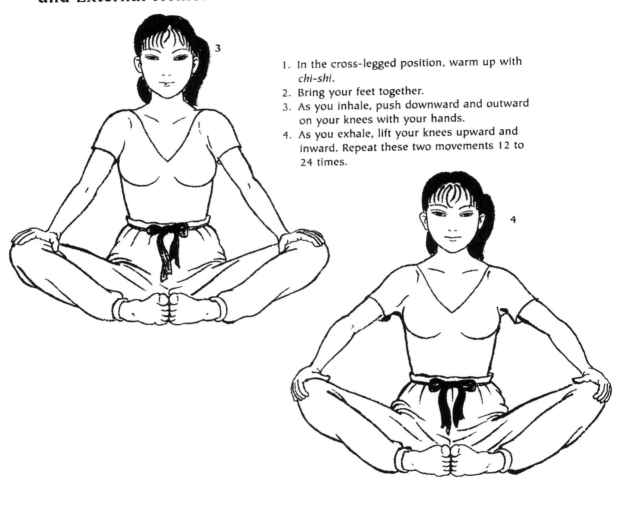

1. In the cross-legged position, warm up with *chi-shi*.
2. Bring your feet together.
3. As you inhale, push downward and outward on your knees with your hands.
4. As you exhale, lift your knees upward and inward. Repeat these two movements 12 to 24 times.

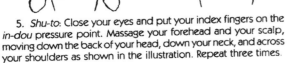

5. *Shu-to*: Close your eyes and put your index fingers on the *in-dou* pressure point. Massage your forehead and your scalp, moving down the back of your head, down your neck, and across your shoulders as shown in the illustration. Repeat three times.

6. *Shun-yo*: Sit on a chair and lift both of your arms up, back, and over your head with your wrists bent. Lift your feet off the floor and bend your toes. Inhale slowly and stretch your back. Then exhale while you bring your arms down to your sides and relax your entire body. Repeat twice.

5. Keeping your feet together, hold your knees with your hands and move your body from left to right three to nine times, as illustrated. Try to keep your heels and your rectum lifted upward.

5

6

Warm up with *chi-shi*

1. *Be-mu*: Stand up, sit on a chair, or sit cross-legged on the floor with your eyes closed.
2. *Chang-tsuo*: Calm your mind.
3. *Tsuo-shou*: Put your palms together and rub them up and down until they feel warm.

4. *Bou-chee*: With your hands spread apart as if you were holding a big ball in front of you, inhale through your nose. Exhale through your mouth while bringing your hands back together.

6. Hold onto your feet and rock your body back and forth three to nine times.
7. Cool down with *shu-kon*.

Cool down with *shu-kon*

1. *Ko-chi*: Make a chewing motion with your mouth five to 100 times.
2. *Tu-na*: Sit on a chair or sit cross-legged on the floor with your eyes closed. Calm your mind. Inhale through your nose and hold your breath for two seconds. While you are holding your breath, imagine that *chi* is flowing from your brain and down your spinal cord and lower back. Exhale slowly through your mouth. When you breathe out, imagine that you are releasing the old *chi* from your body. When you breathe in, imagine that you are inhaling fresh *chi* from nature.

3. *Su-wien*: Wipe the inside of your mouth with your tongue three times. Keeping your tongue behind your upper front teeth, inhale through your mouth. Close your lips and move the air around with your lips and cheeks as if you were cleaning your mouth with it. Do this five to 10 times. If saliva begins to collect in your mouth while you are doing this, swallow it.
4. *Shi-yen*: As you inhale, put your index fingers on the *in-dou* pressure point and massage along your eyebrows until you reach the *tai-you* pressure points. Continue massaging your face until you reach the *hin-sha* pressure points and then massage your neck and chest as shown in the illustration. Repeat three times.

Specific Breathing Techniques to Prevent and Treat Respiratory-System Disorders

The Common Cold and Viruses

1. For Prevention and Treatment: *Ree-jeng-reng-chang-shong*

1. In the most comfortable position for you—either standing, sitting, or lying down on the floor—warm up with *chi-shi*.
2. Gargle with your saliva five times to cleanse your mouth.
3. Keeping the saliva in your mouth, wipe out the inside of your mouth with your tongue.

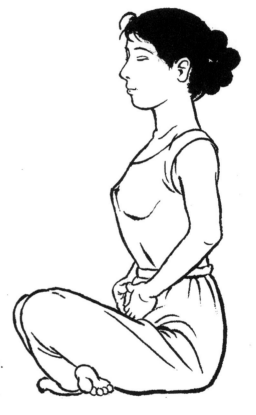

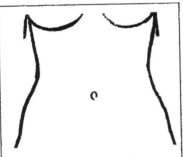

- *Ki-kai* is the pressure point located approximately one inch below your navel.

4. With your tongue held behind your teeth, swallow the saliva with your mouth closed.
5. Inhale deeply through your nose and imagine that you are drawing in *chi* and guiding it to the *ki-kai* pressure point. As you exhale, try to guide the *chi* up through your back and into your brain. Repeat 80 to 300 times.
6. Cool down with *shu-kon*.

④   ⑤  ⑥

5. *Shu-to*: Close your eyes and put your index fingers on the *in-dou* pressure point. Massage your forehead and your scalp, moving down the back of your head, down your neck, and across your shoulders as shown in the illustration. Repeat three times.

6. *Shun-yo*: Sit on a chair and lift both of your arms up, back, and over your head with your wrists bent. Lift your feet off the floor and bend your toes. Inhale slowly and stretch your back. Then exhale while you bring your arms down to your sides and relax your entire body. Repeat twice.

2. For Fever and Sore Thoat: *Uwa-gu-twuo-on*

1. In the cross-legged position, warm up with *chi-shi*.

2. Close your eyes and straighten your back. Pull your elbows in and hold your hands directly above your knees.

Warm up with *chi-shi*

1. *Be-mu*: Stand up, sit on a chair, or sit cross-legged on the floor with your eyes closed.
2. *Chang-tsuo*: Calm your mind.
3. *Tsuo-shou*: Put your palms together and rub them up and down until they feel warm.

4. *Bou-chee*: With your hands spread apart as if you were holding a big ball in front of you, inhale through your nose. Exhale through your mouth while bringing your hands back together.

2

Cool down with *shu-kon*

1. *Ko-chi*: Make a chewing motion with your mouth five to 100 times.
2. *Tu-na*: Sit on a chair or sit cross-legged on the floor with your eyes closed. Calm your mind. Inhale through your nose and hold your breath for two seconds. While you are holding your breath, imagine that *chi* is flowing from your brain and down your spinal cord and lower back. Exhale slowly through your mouth. When you breathe out, imagine that you are releasing the old *chi* from your body. When you breathe in, imagine that you are inhaling fresh *chi* from nature.

3. *Su-wien*: Wipe the inside of your mouth with your tongue three times. Keeping your tongue behind your upper front teeth, inhale through your mouth. Close your lips and move the air around with your lips and cheeks as if you were cleaning your mouth with it. Do this five to 10 times. If saliva begins to collect in your mouth while you are doing this, swallow it.
4. *Shi-yen*: As you inhale, put your index fingers on the *in-dou* pressure point and massage along your eyebrows until you reach the *tai-you* pressure points. Continue massaging your face until you reach the *hin-sha* pressure points and then massage your neck and chest as shown in the illustration. Repeat three times.

3

Tilt your head back, pointing your chin up to the sky. At the same time, lift your hands and massage the *shou-shou* pressure points with your index fingers.

Cool down by doing the *ko-chi*, *tu-na*, and *su-wien* steps of *shu-kon* six times. Do the entire exercise three times a day — morning, noon, and evening.

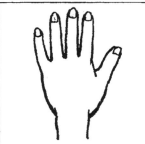

- *Shou-shou* are the pressure points located under your thumbnails.

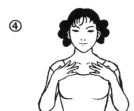

5. *Shu-to*: Close your eyes and put your index fingers on the *in-dou* pressure point. Massage your forehead and your scalp, moving down the back of your head, down your neck, and across your shoulders as shown in the illustration. Repeat three times.

6. *Shun-yo*: Sit on a chair and lift both of your arms up, back, and over your head with your wrists bent. Lift your feet off the floor and bend your toes. Inhale slowly and stretch your back. Then exhale while you bring your arms down to your sides and relax your entire body. Repeat twice.

3. For Headache and Runny Nose: *Gan-you-fa*

1. In the standing or sitting position, warm up with *chi-shi*.

• *In-dou* is the pressure point between your eyebrows.

Warm up with *chi-shi*

1. *Be-mu*: Stand up, sit on a chair, or sit cross-legged on the floor with your eyes closed.
2. *Chang-tsuo*: Calm your mind.
3. *Tsuo-shou*: Put your palms together and rub them up and down until they feel warm.

4. *Bou-chee*: With your hands spread apart as if you were holding a big ball in front of you, inhale through your nose. Exhale through your mouth while bringing your hands back together.

2. With your thumbs and index fingers, massage your earlobes as if you were washing them. Do this 12 to 24 times.
3. Massage your face 12 to 24 times with *shi-yen* (step 4 of the *shu-kon* cool-down exercise).

4. Place the index finger and middle finger of your right hand on the *in-dou* pressure point. Massage the sides of your nose with your thumb and ring finger 14 times.

Cool down with *shu-kon*

1. *Ko-chi*: Make a chewing motion with your mouth five to 100 times.
2. *Tu-na*: Sit on a chair or sit cross-legged on the floor with your eyes closed. Calm your mind. Inhale through your nose and hold your breath for two seconds. While you are holding your breath, imagine that *chi* is flowing from your brain and down your spinal cord and lower back. Exhale slowly through your mouth. When you breathe out, imagine that you are releasing the old *chi* from your body. When you breathe in, imagine that you are inhaling fresh *chi* from nature.

3. *Su-wien*: Wipe the inside of your mouth with your tongue three times. Keeping your tongue behind your upper front teeth, inhale through your mouth. Close your lips and move the air around with your lips and cheeks as if you were cleaning your mouth with it. Do this five to 10 times. If saliva begins to collect in your mouth while you are doing this, swallow it.
4. *Shi-yen*: As you inhale, put your index fingers on the *in-dou* pressure point and massage along your eyebrows until you reach the *tai-you* pressure points. Continue massaging your face until you reach the *hin-sha* pressure points and then massage your neck and chest as shown in the illustration. Repeat three times.

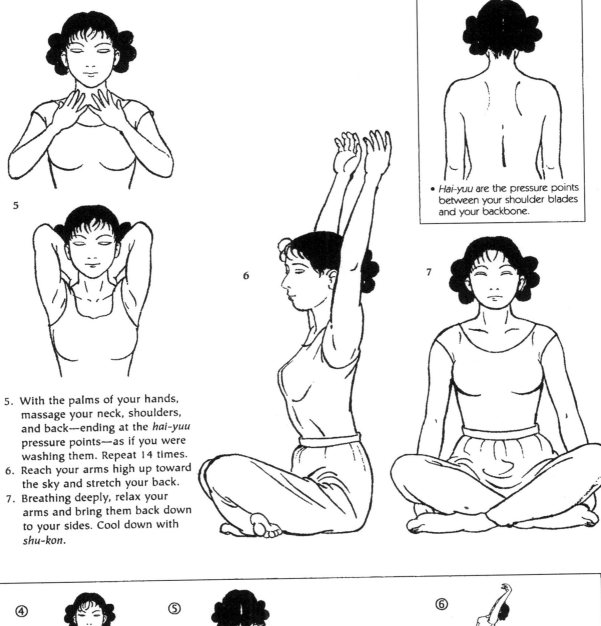

• *Hai-yuu* are the pressure points between your shoulder blades and your backbone.

5. With the palms of your hands, massage your neck, shoulders, and back—ending at the *hai-yuu* pressure points—as if you were washing them. Repeat 14 times.
6. Reach your arms high up toward the sky and stretch your back.
7. Breathing deeply, relax your arms and bring them back down to your sides. Cool down with *shu-kon*.

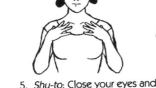

5. *Shu-to*: Close your eyes and put your index fingers on the *in-dou* pressure point. Massage your forehead and your scalp, moving down the back of your head, down your neck, and across your shoulders as shown in the illustration. Repeat three times.

6. *Shun-yo*: Sit on a chair and lift both of your arms up, back, and over your head with your wrists bent. Lift your feet off the floor and bend your toes. Inhale slowly and stretch your back. Then exhale while you bring your arms down to your sides and relax your entire body. Repeat twice.

For Chronic Bronchitis: *Kou-shunn-da-pei*

1. In the standing position, relax your joints and breathe gently. Then warm up with *chi-shi*.

Warm up with *chi-shi*

1. *Be-mu*: Stand up, sit on a chair, or sit cross-legged on the floor with your eyes closed.
2. *Chang-tsuo*: Calm your mind.
3. *Tsuo-shou*: Put your palms together and rub them up and down until they feel warm.

4. *Bou-chee*: With your hands spread apart as if you were holding a big ball in front of you, inhale through your nose. Exhale through your mouth while bringing your hands back together.

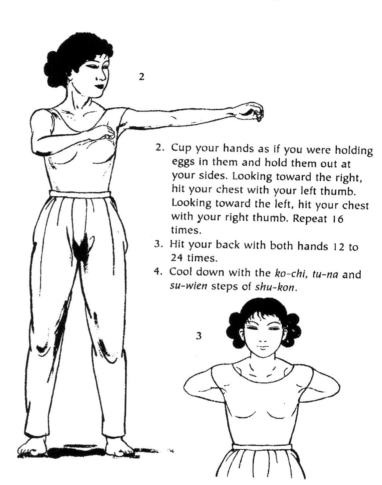

2. Cup your hands as if you were holding eggs in them and hold them out at your sides. Looking toward the right, hit your chest with your left thumb. Looking toward the left, hit your chest with your right thumb. Repeat 16 times.
3. Hit your back with both hands 12 to 24 times.
4. Cool down with the *ko-chi*, *tu-na* and *su-wien* steps of *shu-kon*.

Cool down with *shu-kon*

1. *Ko-chi*: Make a chewing motion with your mouth five to 100 times.
2. *Tu-na*: Sit on a chair or sit cross-legged on the floor with your eyes closed. Calm your mind. Inhale through your nose and hold your breath for two seconds. While you are holding your breath, imagine that *chi* is flowing from your brain and down your spinal cord and lower back. Exhale slowly through your mouth. When you breathe out, imagine that you are releasing the old *chi* from your body. When you breathe in, imagine that you are inhaling fresh *chi* from nature.

3. *Su-wien*: Wipe the inside of your mouth with your tongue three times. Keeping your tongue behind your upper front teeth, inhale through your mouth. Close your lips and move the air around with your lips and cheeks as if you were cleaning your mouth with it. Do this five to 10 times. If saliva begins to collect in your mouth while you are doing this, swallow it.
4. *Shi-yen*: As you inhale, put your index fingers on the *in-dou* pressure point and massage along your eyebrows until you reach the *tai-you* pressure points. Continue massaging your face until you reach the *hin-sha* pressure points and then massage your neck and chest as shown in the illustration. Repeat three times.

For Asthma: *Chu-chi-jun-pi*

2, 3

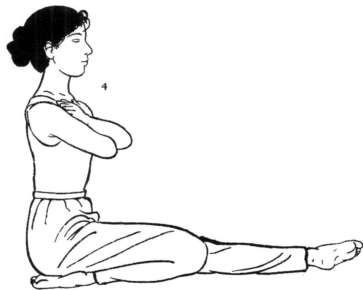

4

1. In the cross-legged position, warm up with *chi-shi*.
2. Bend your right leg under you and keep your left leg extended, pointing your toes toward the floor.
3. Place your hands on the floor behind you and arch your back. Take a deep breath.
4. Straighten your back and cross your arms in front of your chest. Hit your chest with the palms of your hands six to 12 times.
5. Repeat with your left leg bent under you and your right leg extended.
6. Repeat steps 2 through 5 six to 12 times.
7. Cool down with *shu-kon*.

④

⑤

⑥

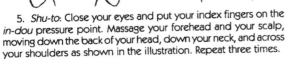

5. *Shu-to*: Close your eyes and put your index fingers on the *in-dou* pressure point. Massage your forehead and your scalp, moving down the back of your head, down your neck, and across your shoulders as shown in the illustration. Repeat three times.

6. *Shun-yo*: Sit on a chair and lift both of your arms up, back, and over your head with your wrists bent. Lift your feet off the floor and bend your toes. Inhale slowly and stretch your back. Then exhale while you bring your arms down to your sides and relax your entire body. Repeat twice.

Specific Breathing Techniques to Prevent and Treat Heart and Circulatory Disorders

High Blood Pressure

1. For Dizziness and Headaches: *Shou-ha-hun-rei*

1. In the cross-legged position, warm up with *chi-shi*.

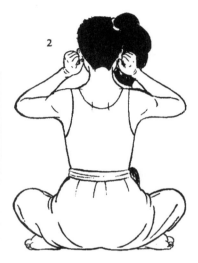

2. With your thumbs and index fingers, massage your ears as illustrated. As you massage downward, inhale. When you reach the end of your earlobes, exhale. Repeat 12 times.

Warm up with *chi-shi*

1. *Be-mu*: Stand up, sit on a chair, or sit cross-legged on the floor with your eyes closed.

2. *Chang-tsuo*: Calm your mind.

3. *Tsuo-shou*: Put your palms together and rub them up and down until they feel warm.

4. *Bou-chee*: With your hands spread apart as if you were holding a big ball in front of you, inhale through your nose. Exhale through your mouth while bringing your hands back together.

---

3. Massage your neck as if you were washing it. As you did in step 2, inhale as you massage downward and exhale when you reach the end. Repeat 12 times.

4. Cool down by doing the *shun-yo* step of *shu-kon* three times.

Cool down with *shu-kon*

1. *Ko-chi*: Make a chewing motion with your mouth five to 100 times.

2. *Tu-na*: Sit on a chair or sit cross-legged on the floor with your eyes closed. Calm your mind. Inhale through your nose and hold your breath for two seconds. While you are holding your breath, imagine that *chi* is flowing from your brain and down your spinal cord and lower back. Exhale slowly through your mouth. When you breathe out, imagine that you are releasing the old *chi* from your body. When you breathe in, imagine that you are inhaling fresh *chi* from nature.

3. *Su-wien*: Wipe the inside of your mouth with your tongue three times. Keeping your tongue behind your upper front teeth, inhale through your mouth. Close your lips and move the air around with your lips and cheeks as if you were cleaning your mouth with it. Do this five to 10 times. If saliva begins to collect in your mouth while you are doing this, swallow it.

4. *Shi-yen*: As you inhale, put your index fingers on the *in-dou* pressure point and massage along your eyebrows until you reach the *tai-you* pressure points. Continue massaging your face until you reach the *hin-sha* pressure points and then massage your neck and chest as shown in the illustration. Repeat three times.

2. For Flushed Face, Nervousness, and Nausea Associated With High Blood Pressure: *Tuo-tie-an-ju*

1. In the sitting position, warm up with *chi-shi*.
2. Breathing deeply, push the palm of your left hand up toward the sky and rest your right hand on your knee with the palm facing up.
3. Exchange hands. As you bring your left hand down, imagine that you are trying to bring the sun and the moon down to your knee. As you raise your right hand toward the sky, imagine that you are releasing the sickness in your body. Follow this movement with your eyes. Alternating hands, repeat 12 to 24 times on each side.
4. Cool down with *shu-kon*, repeating each step six times.

2

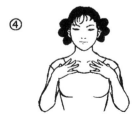

5. *Shu-to*: Close your eyes and put your index fingers on the *in-dou* pressure point. Massage your forehead and your scalp, moving down the back of your head, down your neck, and across your shoulders as shown in the illustration. Repeat three times.

6. *Shun-yo*: Sit on a chair and lift both of your arms up, back, and over your head with your wrists bent. Lift your feet off the floor and bend your toes. Inhale slowly and stretch your back. Then exhale while you bring your arms down to your sides and relax your entire body. Repeat twice.

Low Blood Pressure

1. For Fatigue Due to Low Blood Pressure: *Muon-fu-shi-woi* and *Bo-to-din-zu*

1. In the standing position, warm up with *chi-shi*.

Warm up with *chi-shi*

1. *Be-mu*: Stand up, sit on a chair, or sit cross-legged on the floor with your eyes closed.
2. *Chang-tsuo*: Calm your mind.
3. *Tsuo-shou*: Put your palms together and rub them up and down until they feel warm.

4. *Bou-chee*: With your hands spread apart as if you were holding a big ball in front of you, inhale through your nose. Exhale through your mouth while bringing your hands back together.

Cool down with *shu-kon*

1. *Ko-chi*: Make a chewing motion with your mouth five to 100 times.
2. *Tu-na*: Sit on a chair or sit cross-legged on the floor with your eyes closed. Calm your mind. Inhale through your nose and hold your breath for two seconds. While you are holding your breath, imagine that *chi* is flowing from your brain and down your spinal cord and lower back. Exhale slowly through your mouth. When you breathe out, imagine that you are releasing the old *chi* from your body. When you breathe in, imagine that you are inhaling fresh *chi* from nature.

3. *Su-wien*: Wipe the inside of your mouth with your tongue three times. Keeping your tongue behind your upper front teeth, inhale through your mouth. Close your lips and move the air around with your lips and cheeks as if you were cleaning your mouth with it. Do this five to 10 times. If saliva begins to collect in your mouth while you are doing this, swallow it.
4. *Shi-yen*: As you inhale, put your index fingers on the *in-dou* pressure point and massage along your eyebrows until you reach the *tai-you* pressure points. Continue massaging your face until you reach the *hin-sha* pressure points and then massage your neck and chest as shown in the illustration. Repeat three times.

4, 5

2. Bring your left hand forward, pointing up. At the same time, move your right hand down and back, turning your head to watch it.

3. Breathing deeply, alternate the position of your hands as you take 12 to 24 steps forward. Walk at a natural pace, not too slow and not too fast. As you walk, turn your head from side to side to watch the movement of the hand that you are moving behind you.

4. Put your hands on the back of your neck as illustrated and stand on your toes with your legs apart.

5. Lift yourself up and down on your toes, without letting your heels touch the ground. As you lift yourself up, imagine that you are lifting your stomach and rectum. Repeat seven times.

6. Cool down with the *shi-yen* and *shun-yo* steps of *shou-kon*.

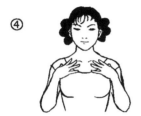

④

⑤

⑥

5. *Shu-to*: Close your eyes and put your index fingers on the *in-dou* pressure point. Massage your forehead and your scalp, moving down the back of your head, down your neck, and across your shoulders as shown in the illustration. Repeat three times.

6. *Shun-yo*: Sit on a chair and lift both of your arms up, back, and over your head with your wrists bent. Lift your feet off the floor and bend your toes. Inhale slowly and stretch your back. Then exhale while you bring your arms down to your sides and relax your entire body. Repeat twice.

2. For Headache and Backache Due to Low Blood Pressure: *Woo-long-han-ti* and *Bei-chi-chon-din*

1. In the cross-legged position, warm up with *chi-shi*.

2. With your arms and legs slightly apart, position yourself on your hands and knees as illustrated.

3. Inhaling through your nose, reach forward, pressing your upper body toward the ground and stretching your back. At the same time, press the tops of your feet into the ground.

Warm up with *chi-shi*

1. *Be-mu*: Stand up, sit on a chair, or sit cross-legged on the floor with your eyes closed.
2. *Chang-tsuo*: Calm your mind.
3. *Tsuo-shou*: Put your palms together and rub them up and down until they feel warm.

4. *Bou-chee*: With your hands spread apart as if you were holding a big ball in front of you, inhale through your nose. Exhale through your mouth while bringing your hands back together.

Cool down with *shu-kon*

1. *Ko-chi*: Make a chewing motion with your mouth five to 100 times.
2. *Tu-na*: Sit on a chair or sit cross-legged on the floor with your eyes closed. Calm your mind. Inhale through your nose and hold your breath for two seconds. While you are holding your breath, imagine that *chi* is flowing from your brain and down your spinal cord and lower back. Exhale slowly through your mouth. When you breathe out, imagine that you are releasing the old *chi* from your body. When you breathe in, imagine that you are inhaling fresh *chi* from nature.

3. *Su-wien*: Wipe the inside of your mouth with your tongue three times. Keeping your tongue behind your upper front teeth, inhale through your mouth. Close your lips and move the air around with your lips and cheeks as if you were cleaning your mouth with it. Do this five to 10 times. If saliva begins to collect in your mouth while you are doing this, swallow it.
4. *Shi-yen*: As you inhale, put your index fingers on the *in-dou* pressure point and massage along your eyebrows until you reach the *tai-you* pressure points. Continue massaging your face until you reach the *hin-sha* pressure points and then massage your neck and chest as shown in the illustration. Repeat three times.

4. Exhale through your mouth as you return to the hands-and-knees position as illustrated in step 2.
5. Repeat steps 3 and 4 six times.
6. Sit on a chair with your toes touching the ground and your legs slightly apart.
7. Bend over as illustrated, forcefully pressing your hands toward the ground. Repeat this motion 12 to 24 times.
8. Cool down with *shu-kon*.

6, 7

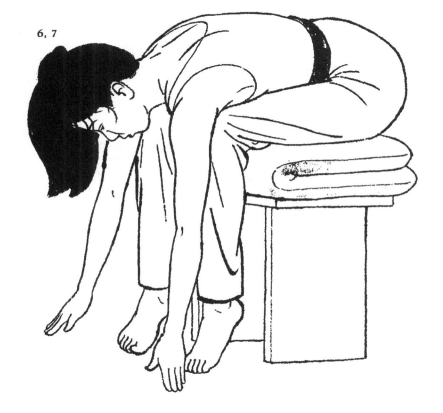

  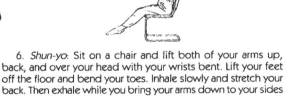

5. *Shu-to*: Close your eyes and put your index fingers on the *in-dou* pressure point. Massage your forehead and your scalp, moving down the back of your head, down your neck, and across your shoulders as shown in the illustration. Repeat three times.

6. *Shun-yo*: Sit on a chair and lift both of your arms up, back, and over your head with your wrists bent. Lift your feet off the floor and bend your toes. Inhale slowly and stretch your back. Then exhale while you bring your arms down to your sides and relax your entire body. Repeat twice.

Angina

1. For Pressure on the Heart: *Fei-je-jan-yo*

1. In the standing position, warm up with *chi-shi*.

2. Form a T with your feet, turning your right foot out and positioning your left food perpendicular to it. Stand tall, but stay relaxed.

3. Extend the index and middle fingers of your right hand as if you were making them into the blade of a knife. Rest your left arm on your back and turn your head toward the left. Inhaling deeply through your nose, swing your right arm up over your head. Swing your right arm down as you exhale.

4. Switch arms and repeat step 3. Face right as you swing your left arm up and down.

5. Repeat nine times.

6. Cool down with the *ko-chi, tu-na*, and *su-wien* steps of *shu-kon*.

2, 3

Warm up with *chi-shi*

1. *Be-mu*: Stand up, sit on a chair, or sit cross-legged on the floor with your eyes closed.

2. *Chang-tsuo*: Calm your mind.

3. *Tsuo-shou*: Put your palms together and rub them up and down until they feel warm.

4. *Bou-chee*: With your hands spread apart as if you were holding a big ball in front of you, inhale through your nose. Exhale through your mouth while bringing your hands back together.

Cool down with *shu-kon*

1. *Ko-chi*: Make a chewing motion with your mouth five to 100 times.

2. *Tu-na*: Sit on a chair or sit cross-legged on the floor with your eyes closed. Calm your mind. Inhale through your nose and hold your breath for two seconds. While you are holding your breath, imagine that *chi* is flowing from your brain and down your spinal cord and lower back. Exhale slowly through your mouth. When you breathe out, imagine that you are releasing the old *chi* from your body. When you breathe in, imagine that you are inhaling fresh *chi* from nature.

3. *Su-wien*: Wipe the inside of your mouth with your tongue three times. Keeping your tongue behind your upper front teeth, inhale through your mouth. Close your lips and move the air around with your lips and cheeks as if you were cleaning your mouth with it. Do this five to 10 times. If saliva begins to collect in your mouth while you are doing this, swallow it.

4. *Shi-yen*: As you inhale, put your index fingers on the *in-dou* pressure point and massage along your eyebrows until you reach the *tai-you* pressure points. Continue massaging your face until you reach the *hin-sha* pressure points and then massage your neck and chest as shown in the illustration. Repeat three times.

2. For Chest Pressure or Pain:
Ton-zu-bai-guan-in

1. In the standing position, warm up with *chi-shi*.
2. Link your hands together, palms up, in front of your stomach. Bend your head down.
3. Inhale through your nose and hold your breath for two seconds. Inhale slightly and then exhale through your mouth. Repeat 12 to 24 times.
4. Cool down with *shu-kon*.

5. *Shu-to*: Close your eyes and put your index fingers on the *in-dou* pressure point. Massage your forehead and your scalp, moving down the back of your head, down your neck, and across your shoulders as shown in the illustration. Repeat three times.

6. *Shun-yo*: Sit on a chair and lift both of your arms up, back, and over your head with your wrists bent. Lift your feet off the floor and bend your toes. Inhale slowly and stretch your back. Then exhale while you bring your arms down to your sides and relax your entire body. Repeat twice.

Heart Attack

1. For Chest Pressure and Anxiety: *An-chi-ti-chi*

1. In the cross-legged position, warm up with *chi-shi*.

Warm up with *chi-shi*

1. *Be-mu*: Stand up, sit on a chair, or sit cross-legged on the floor with your eyes closed.
2. *Chang-tsuo*: Calm your mind.
3. *Tsuo-shou*: Put your palms together and rub them up and down until they feel warm.

4. *Bou-chee*: With your hands spread apart as if you were holding a big ball in front of you, inhale through your nose. Exhale through your mouth while bringing your hands back together.

2. Place your hands on your knees and concentrate on your *dan-chu* pressure point. Inhale and imagine that you are guiding your breath down through your *dan-chu* and *ki-kai* pressure points and back up into your head. Exhale. Repeat for five to 20 minutes.

Cool down with *shu-kon*

1. *Ko-chi*: Make a chewing motion with your mouth five to 100 times.
2. *Tu-na*: Sit on a chair or sit cross-legged on the floor with your eyes closed. Calm your mind. Inhale through your nose and hold your breath for two seconds. While you are holding your breath, imagine that *chi* is flowing from your brain and down your spinal cord and lower back. Exhale slowly through your mouth. When you breathe out, imagine that you are releasing the old *chi* from your body. When you breathe in, imagine that you are inhaling fresh *chi* from nature.

3. *Su-wien*: Wipe the inside of your mouth with your tongue three times. Keeping your tongue behind your upper front teeth, inhale through your mouth. Close your lips and move the air around with your lips and cheeks as if you were cleaning your mouth with it. Do this five to 10 times. If saliva begins to collect in your mouth while you are doing this, swallow it.
4. *Shi-yen*: As you inhale, put your index fingers on the *in-dou* pressure point and massage along your eyebrows until you reach the *tai-you* pressure points. Continue massaging your face until you reach the *hin-sha* pressure points and then massage your neck and chest as shown in the illustration. Repeat three times.

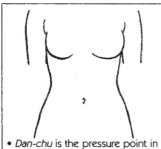

- *Dan-chu* is the pressure point in the center of your chest.
- *Ki-kai* is the pressure point located approximately one inch below your navel.

3. Looking at your left thumb, raise your right shoulder. Inhale, bringing the air down through your chest and into your stomach. Exhale. Repeat 12 to 24 times, breathing naturally.
4. Looking at your right thumb, raise your left shoulder. Repeat step 3.
5. Repeat 12 to 24 times steps 3 and 4.
6. Cool down with *shu-kon*.

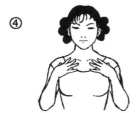

5. *Shu-to*: Close your eyes and put your index fingers on the *in-dou* pressure point. Massage your forehead and your scalp, moving down the back of your head, down your neck, and across your shoulders as shown in the illustration. Repeat three times.

6. *Shun-yo*: Sit on a chair and lift both of your arms up, back, and over your head with your wrists bent. Lift your feet off the floor and bend your toes. Inhale slowly and stretch your back. Then exhale while you bring your arms down to your sides and relax your entire body. Repeat twice.

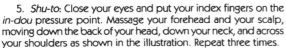

2. For Anxiety or Chest Pain: *Tei-jun-ba-jen*

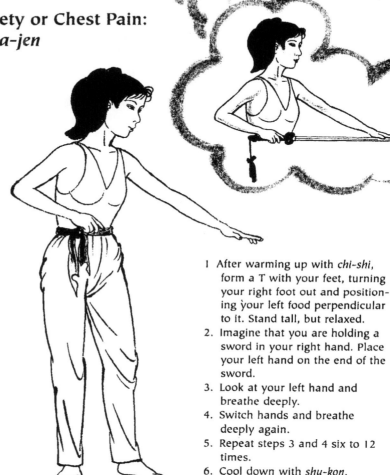

Warm up with *chi-shi*

1. *Be-mu*: Stand up, sit on a chair, or sit cross-legged on the floor with your eyes closed.
2. *Chang-tsuo*: Calm your mind.
3. *Tsuo-shou*: Put your palms together and rub them up and down until they feel warm.

4. *Bou-chee*: With your hands spread apart as if you were holding a big ball in front of you, inhale through your nose. Exhale through your mouth while bringing your hands back together.

1. After warming up with *chi-shi*, form a T with your feet, turning your right foot out and positioning your left food perpendicular to it. Stand tall, but relaxed.
2. Imagine that you are holding a sword in your right hand. Place your left hand on the end of the sword.
3. Look at your left hand and breathe deeply.
4. Switch hands and breathe deeply again.
5. Repeat steps 3 and 4 six to 12 times.
6. Cool down with *shu-kon*.

Cool down with *shu-kon*

1. *Ko-chi*: Make a chewing motion with your mouth five to 100 times.
2. *Tu-na*: Sit on a chair or sit cross-legged on the floor with your eyes closed. Calm your mind. Inhale through your nose and hold your breath for two seconds. While you are holding your breath, imagine that *chi* is flowing from your brain and down your spinal cord and lower back. Exhale slowly through your mouth. When you breathe out, imagine that you are releasing the old *chi* from your body. When you breathe in, imagine that you are inhaling fresh *chi* from nature.

3. *Su-wien*: Wipe the inside of your mouth with your tongue three times. Keeping your tongue behind your upper front teeth, inhale through your mouth. Close your lips and move the air around with your lips and cheeks as if you were cleaning your mouth with it. Do this five to 10 times. If saliva begins to collect in your mouth while you are doing this, swallow it.
4. *Shi-yen*: As you inhale, put your index fingers on the *in-dou* pressure point and massage along your eyebrows until you reach the *tai-you* pressure points. Continue massaging your face until you reach the *hin-sha* pressure points and then massage your neck and chest as shown in the illustration. Repeat three times.

Specific Breathing Techniques to Prevent Urinary and Sexual Disorders

Kidney Disease

1. For Fatigue and Difficulty in Urinating: *Won-ha-shen-nan*

1. In the cross-legged position, warm up with *chi-shi*.
2. Place your hands on your back as illustrated. Inhale through your nose as you move your hands up. Exhale through your mouth as you move your hands down. Repeat 20 to 40 times. As you do this exercise, imagine that there is a fire in your body. The *shimotanden* pressure point —the spot where *chi* is being drawn—will feel warm.
3. Cool down by doing the *shun-yo* step of *shu-kon* twice.

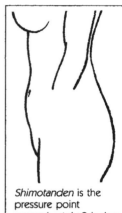

Shimotanden is the pressure point approximately 3 inches below your navel.

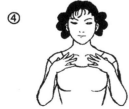

5. *Shu-to*: Close your eyes and put your index fingers on the *in-dou* pressure point. Massage your forehead and your scalp, moving down the back of your head, down your neck, and across your shoulders as shown in the illustration. Repeat three times.

6. *Shun-yo*: Sit on a chair and lift both of your arms up, back, and over your head with your wrists bent. Lift your feet off the floor and bend your toes. Inhale slowly and stretch your back. Then exhale while you bring your arms down to your sides and relax your entire body. Repeat twice.

2. For Fatigue Associated With Kidney Disease: *Pei-ta-chuen-shen*

1. Standing with your legs slightly apart, warm up with *chi-shi*.

2, 3

4

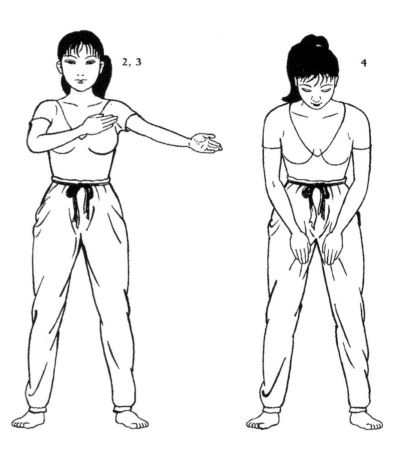

Warm up with *chi-shi*

1. *Be-mu*: Stand up, sit on a chair, or sit cross-legged on the floor with your eyes closed.
2. *Chang-tsuo*: Calm your mind.
3. *Tsuo-shou*: Put your palms together and rub them up and down until they feel warm.

4. *Bou-chee*: With your hands spread apart as if you were holding a big ball in front of you, inhale through your nose. Exhale through your mouth while bringing your hands back together.

Cool down with *shu-kon*

1. *Ko-chi*: Make a chewing motion with your mouth five to 100 times.
2. *Tu-na*: Sit on a chair or sit cross-legged on the floor with your eyes closed. Calm your mind. Inhale through your nose and hold your breath for two seconds. While you are holding your breath, imagine that *chi* is flowing from your brain and down your spinal cord and lower back. Exhale slowly through your mouth. When you breathe out, imagine that you are releasing the old *chi* from your body. When you breathe in, imagine that you are inhaling fresh *chi* from nature.

3. *Su-wien*: Wipe the inside of your mouth with your tongue three times. Keeping your tongue behind your upper front teeth, inhale through your mouth. Close your lips and move the air around with your lips and cheeks as if you were cleaning your mouth with it. Do this five to 10 times. If saliva begins to collect in your mouth while you are doing this, swallow it.
4. *Shi-yen*: As you inhale, put your index fingers on the *in-dou* pressure point and massage along your eyebrows until you reach the *tai-you* pressure points. Continue massaging your face until you reach the *hin-sha* pressure points and then massage your neck and chest as shown in the illustration. Repeat three times.

For Discomfort While Urinating:
Fang-shao-four-shi

1. Warm up with *chi-shi*.
2. Sit cross-legged on the floor. If you can't do this comfortably, stretch your legs out in front of you. With your fists, push down on the floor, bending forward slightly. Inhale deeply and raise your left shoulder, imagining that you are a tiger ready to strike an animal. While you do this, look down at your right fist and try to lift your urethra.

3. As you exhale, switch sides. As you inhale, raise your right shoulder while looking down at your left fist.
4. Repeat 12 to 24 times steps 2 and 3.
5. Keeping both fists on the floor, breathe deeply, as a tiger would.
6. Cool down with the *ko-chi, tu-na, su-wien,* and *shun-yo* steps of *shu-kon.*

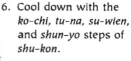

2. Holding your arms as illustrated, use the palm of your right hand to hit the left side of your chest and your left shoulder. Continue down your left arm, hitting your forearm and wrist. Then come back up, hitting your left forearm, shoulder, and chest.
3. Reverse the procedure, using the palm of your left hand to hit the right side of your chest, your right shoulder, and your right arm.
4. Using both hands, move down your entire body, hitting the front of your chest, your stomach, the insides of your legs, and your ankles. Then come back up the outsides of your legs.
5. Cool down with *shu-kon.*

5. *Shu-to:* Close your eyes and put your index fingers on the *in-dou* pressure point. Massage your forehead and your scalp, moving down the back of your head, down your neck, and across your shoulders as shown in the illustration. Repeat three times.

6. *Shun-yo:* Sit on a chair and lift both of your arms up, back, and over your head with your wrists bent. Lift your feet off the floor and bend your toes. Inhale slowly and stretch your back. Then exhale while you bring your arms down to your sides and relax your entire body. Repeat twice.

Genital Swelling

1. With Swelling Over the Entire Body: *Zou-shi-you-ui*

1. Sit on a chair without back support and warm up with *chi-shi*.

2. With both of your hands, try to pull *chi* up from your stomach.
3. Facing left, pull the *chi* up and out over your right side.

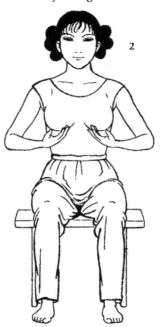

Warm up with *chi-shi*

1. *Be-mu*: Stand up, sit on a chair, or sit cross-legged on the floor with your eyes closed.
2. *Chang-tsuo*: Calm your mind.
3. *Tsuo-shou*: Put your palms together and rub them up and down until they feel warm.

4. *Bou-chee*: With your hands spread apart as if you were holding a big ball in front of you, inhale through your nose. Exhale through your mouth while bringing your hands back together.

---

4. Do the same thing facing right and pulling the *chi* up and out over your left side. Repeat 15 times on each side.
5. Cool down with *shu-kon*.

Cool down with *shu-kon*

1. *Ko-chi*: Make a chewing motion with your mouth five to 100 times.
2. *Tu-na*: Sit on a chair or sit cross-legged on the floor with your eyes closed. Calm your mind. Inhale through your nose and hold your breath for two seconds. While you are holding your breath, imagine that *chi* is flowing from your brain and down your spinal cord and lower back. Exhale slowly through your mouth. When you breathe out, imagine that you are releasing the old *chi* from your body. When you breathe in, imagine that you are inhaling fresh *chi* from nature.

3. *Su-wien*: Wipe the inside of your mouth with your tongue three times. Keeping your tongue behind your upper front teeth, inhale through your mouth. Close your lips and move the air around with your lips and cheeks as if you were cleaning your mouth with it. Do this five to 10 times. If saliva begins to collect in your mouth while you are doing this, swallow it.
4. *Shi-yen*: As you inhale, put your index fingers on the *in-dou* pressure point and massage along your eyebrows until you reach the *tai-you* pressure points. Continue massaging your face until you reach the *hin-sha* pressure points and then massage your neck and chest as shown in the illustration. Repeat three times.

2. With Facial Swelling: *Chu-chi-jun-pi*

1. In the cross-legged position, warm up with *chi-shi*.
2. Bend your right leg under you and keep your left leg extended, pointing your toes toward the floor.
3. Place your hands on the floor behind you and arch your back. Take a deep breath.
4. Straighten your back and cross your arms in front of your chest. Hit your chest with the palms of your hands six to 12 times.
5. Repeat steps 3 and 4 with your left leg bent under you and your right leg extended.
6. Repeat steps 2 through 5 six to 12 times.

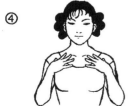

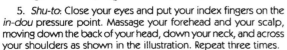

5. *Shu-to*: Close your eyes and put your index fingers on the *in-dou* pressure point. Massage your forehead and your scalp, moving down the back of your head, down your neck, and across your shoulders as shown in the illustration. Repeat three times.

6. *Shun-yo*: Sit on a chair and lift both of your arms up, back, and over your head with your wrists bent. Lift your feet off the floor and bend your toes. Inhale slowly and stretch your back. Then exhale while you bring your arms down to your sides and relax your entire body. Repeat twice.

3. With Swelling Over the Lower Body: *Shen-zu-an-chi*

1. In the cross-legged position, warm up with *chi-shi*.

2. Extend your legs in front of you.
3. Massage your legs with both hands. Inhale deeply as you massage down from your knees to your toes. Exhale deeply as you massage back up from your toes to your knees. Repeat 12 to 24 times.
4. Cool down with the *ko-chi, su-wien,* and *shun-yo* steps of *shu-kon.*

Warm up with *chi-shi*

1. *Be-mu:* Stand up, sit on a chair, or sit cross-legged on the floor with your eyes closed.
2. *Chang-tsuo:* Calm your mind.
3. *Tsuo-shou:* Put your palms together and rub them up and down until they feel warm.

4. *Bou-chee:* With your hands spread apart as if you were holding a big ball in front of you, inhale through your nose. Exhale through your mouth while bringing your hands back together.

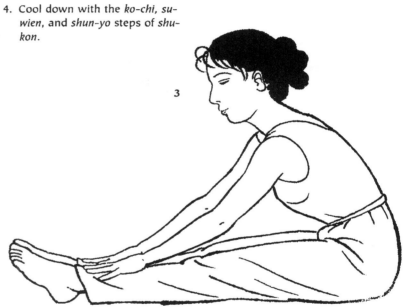

3

Cool down with *shu-kon*

1. *Ko-chi:* Make a chewing motion with your mouth five to 100 times.
2. *Tu-na:* Sit on a chair or sit cross-legged on the floor with your eyes closed. Calm your mind. Inhale through your nose and hold your breath for two seconds. While you are holding your breath, imagine that *chi* is flowing from your brain and down your spinal cord and lower back. Exhale slowly through your mouth. When you breathe out, imagine that you are releasing the old *chi* from your body. When you breathe in, imagine that you are inhaling fresh *chi* from nature.

3. *Su-wien:* Wipe the inside of your mouth with your tongue three times. Keeping your tongue behind your upper front teeth, inhale through your mouth. Close your lips and move the air around with your lips and cheeks as if you were cleaning your mouth with it. Do this five to 10 times. If saliva begins to collect in your mouth while you are doing this, swallow it.
4. *Shi-yen:* As you inhale, put your index fingers on the *in-dou* pressure point and massage along your eyebrows until you reach the *tai-you* pressure points. Continue massaging your face until you reach the *hin-sha* pressure points and then massage your neck and chest as shown in the illustration. Repeat three times.

During Kidney Dialysis

1. For Fatigue and Loss of Appetite: *Tui-chowan-wan-yue*

1. In the standing position, warm up with *chi-shi*.
2. Imagine that there is a window on your right side and another on your left side. Turn toward the window on your right side and open it with both hands so you can see the moon.
3. Bring your hands back behind you. Turn and open the window on your left side to see the moon and then bring your hands back behind you.

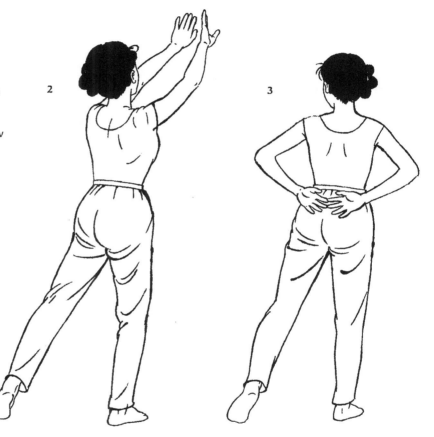

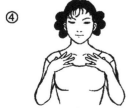  

5. *Shu-to:* Close your eyes and put your index fingers on the *in-dou* pressure point. Massage your forehead and your scalp, moving down the back of your head, down your neck, and across your shoulders as shown in the illustration. Repeat three times.

6. *Shun-yo:* Sit on a chair and lift both of your arms up, back, and over your head with your wrists bent. Lift your feet off the floor and bend your toes. Inhale slowly and stretch your back. Then exhale while you bring your arms down to your sides and relax your entire body. Repeat twice.

4. Repeat steps 2 and 3 three to 12 times. Hit your lower back with both hands.
5. Cool down with *shu-kon*.

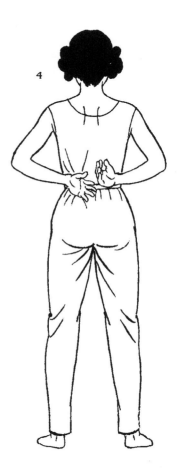

4

Warm up with *chi-shi*

1. *Be-mu*: Stand up, sit on a chair, or sit cross-legged on the floor with your eyes closed.
2. *Chang-tsuo*: Calm your mind.
3. *Tsuo-shou*: Put your palms together and rub them up and down until they feel warm.

4. *Bou-chee*: With your hands spread apart as if you were holding a big ball in front of you, inhale through your nose. Exhale through your mouth while bringing your hands back together.

Cool down with *shu-kon*

1. *Ko-chi*: Make a chewing motion with your mouth five to 100 times.
2. *Tu-na*: Sit on a chair or sit cross-legged on the floor with your eyes closed. Calm your mind. Inhale through your nose and hold your breath for two seconds. While you are holding your breath, imagine that *chi* is flowing from your brain and down your spinal cord and lower back. Exhale slowly through your mouth. When you breathe out, imagine that you are releasing the old *chi* from your body. When you breathe in, imagine that you are inhaling fresh *chi* from nature.

3. *Su-wien*: Wipe the inside of your mouth with your tongue three times. Keeping your tongue behind your upper front teeth, inhale through your mouth. Close your lips and move the air around with your lips and cheeks as if you were cleaning your mouth with it. Do this five to 10 times. If saliva begins to collect in your mouth while you are doing this, swallow it.
4. *Shi-yen*: As you inhale, put your index fingers on the *in-dou* pressure point and massage along your eyebrows until you reach the *tai-you* pressure points. Continue massaging your face until you reach the *hin-sha* pressure points and then massage your neck and chest as shown in the illustration. Repeat three times.

2. For Excessive Fluid Retention During Kidney Dialysis: *Shen-zu-an-chi*

1. In the cross-legged position, warm up with *chi-shi*.
2. Stretch your legs out in front of you.
3. With both hands, massage your legs from your knees to your toes. As you massage down toward your toes, inhale through your nose. As you massage up toward your knees, exhale through your mouth. Repeat 12 to 24 times.
4. Cool down with the *ko-chi*, *su-wien*, and *shun-yo* steps of *shu-kon*.

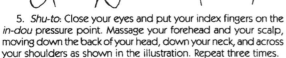

5. *Shu-to*: Close your eyes and put your index fingers on the *in-dou* pressure point. Massage your forehead and your scalp, moving down the back of your head, down your neck, and across your shoulders as shown in the illustration. Repeat three times.

6. *Shun-yo*: Sit on a chair and lift both of your arms up, back, and over your head with your wrists bent. Lift your feet off the floor and bend your toes. Inhale slowly and stretch your back. Then exhale while you bring your arms down to your sides and relax your entire body. Repeat twice.

3. For Low Blood Pressure During Kidney Dialysis: *Gu-shen-wo-inn*

1. In the cross-legged position, warm up with *chi-shi*.
2. Lie down on the floor as illustrated with your right arm under your head. Bend your right knee and extend your left leg.
3. With your left hand, massage around the *ki-kai* pressure point as if you were drawing a figure eight on your stomach. As you massage, breathe deeply 12 to 50 times. Cool down with *shu-kon*.

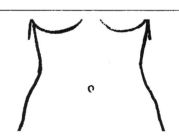

- *Ki-kai* is the pressure point located approximately one inch below your navel.

Warm up with *chi-shi*

1. *Be-mu*: Stand up, sit on a chair, or sit cross-legged on the floor with your eyes closed.
2. *Chang-tsuo*: Calm your mind.
3. *Tsuo-shou*: Put your palms together and rub them up and down until they feel warm.

4. *Bou-chee*: With your hands spread apart as if you were holding a big ball in front of you, inhale through your nose. Exhale through your mouth while bringing your hands back together.

2, 3

Cool down with *shu-kon*

1. *Ko-chi*: Make a chewing motion with your mouth five to 100 times.
2. *Tu-na*: Sit on a chair or sit cross-legged on the floor with your eyes closed. Calm your mind. Inhale through your nose and hold your breath for two seconds. While you are holding your breath, imagine that *chi* is flowing from your brain and down your spinal cord and lower back. Exhale slowly through your mouth. When you breathe out, imagine that you are releasing the old *chi* from your body. When you breathe in, imagine that you are inhaling fresh *chi* from nature.

3. *Su-wien*: Wipe the inside of your mouth with your tongue three times. Keeping your tongue behind your upper front teeth, inhale through your mouth. Close your lips and move the air around with your lips and cheeks as if you were cleaning your mouth with it. Do this five to 10 times. If saliva begins to collect in your mouth while you are doing this, swallow it.
4. *Shi-yen*: As you inhale, put your index fingers on the *in-dou* pressure point and massage along your eyebrows until you reach the *tai-you* pressure points. Continue massaging your face until you reach the *hin-sha* pressure points and then massage your neck and chest as shown in the illustration. Repeat three times.

Specific Breathing Techniques to Prevent Muscular and Skeletal Disorders

Stiffness Caused by Stress

1. For the Neck and Shoulders: *Fun-howan-jan-chi*

1. In the standing position, warm up with *chi-shi*.
2. With your right hand on your stomach, slightly bend your lower back and knees and bring your left palm up as illustrated. As you do this, imagine that you are reaching up to the sky.
3. Switch hands and do the same thing. Repeat six to 24 times on each side.
4. Cool down with *shu-kon*.

5. *Shu-to*: Close your eyes and put your index fingers on the *in-dou* pressure point. Massage your forehead and your scalp, moving down the back of your head, down your neck, and across your shoulders as shown in the illustration. Repeat three times.

6. *Shun-yo*: Sit on a chair and lift both of your arms up, back, and over your head with your wrists bent. Lift your feet off the floor and bend your toes. Inhale slowly and stretch your back. Then exhale while you bring your arms down to your sides and relax your entire body. Repeat twice.

2. For the Shoulders and Lower Back: *Gao-zo-jan-gon*

1. In the sitting position, warm up with *chi-shi*.

2. Following the illustration, imagine that you are preparing to shoot a bow and arrow. Repeat 10 to 50 times on each side.

3. Cool down by doing the *ko-chi, tu-na, su-wien,* and *shun-yo* steps of *shu-kon* three times.

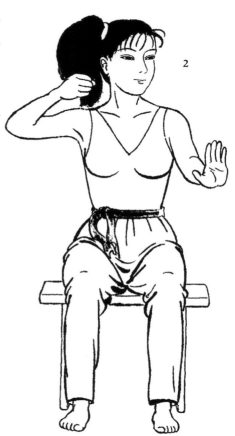

Warm up with *chi-shi*

1. *Be-mu*: Stand up, sit on a chair, or sit cross-legged on the floor with your eyes closed.

2. *Chang-tsuo*: Calm your mind.

3. *Tsuo-shou*: Put your palms together and rub them up and down until they feel warm.

4. *Bou-chee*: With your hands spread apart as if you were holding a big ball in front of you, inhale through your nose. Exhale through your mouth while bringing your hands back together.

Cool down with *shu-kon*

1. *Ko-chi*: Make a chewing motion with your mouth five to 100 times.

2. *Tu-na*: Sit on a chair or sit cross-legged on the floor with your eyes closed. Calm your mind. Inhale through your nose and hold your breath for two seconds. While you are holding your breath, imagine that *chi* is flowing from your brain and down your spinal cord and lower back. Exhale slowly through your mouth. When you breathe out, imagine that you are releasing the old *chi* from your body. When you breathe in, imagine that you are inhaling fresh *chi* from nature.

3. *Su-wien*: Wipe the inside of your mouth with your tongue three times. Keeping your tongue behind your upper front teeth, inhale through your mouth. Close your lips and move the air around with your lips and cheeks as if you were cleaning your mouth with it. Do this five to 10 times. If saliva begins to collect in your mouth while you are doing this, swallow it.

4. *Shi-yen*: As you inhale, put your index fingers on the *in-dou* pressure point and massage along your eyebrows until you reach the *tai-you* pressure points. Continue massaging your face until you reach the *hin-sha* pressure points and then massage your neck and chest as shown in the illustration. Repeat three times.

Neck Injuries

1. For Neck Pain: *Ho-tong-shin-shin*

1. In the standing position, warm up with *chi-shi*.
2. As you inhale through your nose, bend over and reach for your toes, stretching your back. Go only as far as you can without feeling discomfort.
3. Stretch out your neck as a turtle would while exhaling through your mouth. Return to the standing position.
4. Repeat steps 2 and 3 six to 24 times.
5. Cool down with *shu-kon*.

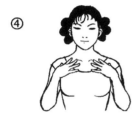

5. *Shu-to*: Close your eyes and put your index fingers on the *in-dou* pressure point. Massage your forehead and your scalp, moving down the back of your head, down your neck, and across your shoulders as shown in the illustration. Repeat three times.

6. *Shun-yo*: Sit on a chair and lift both of your arms up, back, and over your head with your wrists bent. Lift your feet off the floor and bend your toes. Inhale slowly and stretch your back. Then exhale while you bring your arms down to your sides and relax your entire body. Repeat twice.

2. For Neck Stiffness: *Gu-yu-zo-guon*

1. Sitting cross-legged on the floor, warm up with *chi-shi*.

Warm up with *chi-shi*

1. *Be-mu:* Stand up, sit on a chair, or sit cross-legged on the floor with your eyes closed.

2. *Chang-tsuo:* Calm your mind.

3. *Tsuo-shou:* Put your palms together and rub them up and down until they feel warm.

4. *Bou-chee:* With your hands spread apart as if you were holding a big ball in front of you, inhale through your nose. Exhale through your mouth while bringing your hands back together.

---

2. As you inhale through your nose, reach your right hand over your head as if you were trying to pick an apple from a tree. Place your left hand under your right breast with the palm facing up.

3. As you exhale through your mouth, move your right hand under your left breast and reach your left hand over your head.

4. Repeat steps 2 and 3 30 to 50 times.

5. Cool down with *shu-kon*.

Cool down with *shu-kon*

1. *Ko-chi:* Make a chewing motion with your mouth five to 100 times.

2. *Tu-na:* Sit on a chair or sit cross-legged on the floor with your eyes closed. Calm your mind. Inhale through your nose and hold your breath for two seconds. While you are holding your breath, imagine that *chi* is flowing from your brain and down your spinal cord and lower back. Exhale slowly through your mouth. When you breathe out, imagine that you are releasing the old *chi* from your body. When you breathe in, imagine that you are inhaling fresh *chi* from nature.

3. *Su-wien:* Wipe the inside of your mouth with your tongue three times. Keeping your tongue behind your upper front teeth, inhale through your mouth. Close your lips and move the air around with your lips and cheeks as if you were cleaning your mouth with it. Do this five to 10 times. If saliva begins to collect in your mouth while you are doing this, swallow it.

4. *Shi-yen:* As you inhale, put your index fingers on the *in-dou* pressure point and massage along your eyebrows until you reach the *tai-you* pressure points. Continue massaging your face until you reach the *hin-sha* pressure points and then massage your neck and chest as shown in the illustration. Repeat three times.

3. For Discomfort Throughout the Entire Body Due to Neck Injury: *Won-ha-shen-nan*

1. In the cross-legged position, warm up with *chi-shi.*
2. With both hands, massage your lower back. As you massage upward, inhale through your nose. As you massage downward, exhale through your mouth. Imagine that you have a fire in your body and that you are moving the fire toward your navel as you inhale. The *shimotanden* pressure point—the spot where *chi* is being drawn by this exercise—will feel warm. Repeat 20 to 40 times. Cool down with *shu-kon.*

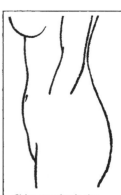

Shimotanden is the pressure point approximately 3 inches below your navel.

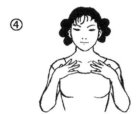

5. *Shu-to:* Close your eyes and put your index fingers on the *in-dou* pressure point. Massage your forehead and your scalp, moving down the back of your head, down your neck, and across your shoulders as shown in the illustration. Repeat three times.

6. *Shun-yo:* Sit on a chair and lift both of your arms up, back, and over your head with your wrists bent. Lift your feet off the floor and bend your toes. Inhale slowly and stretch your back. Then exhale while you bring your arms down to your sides and relax your entire body. Repeat twice.

For Back Pain:
Kao-gowae-twuo-tei

2

1. In the standing position, warm up with *chi-shi*. Using a stick (a cane or umbrella, for example), stand with your legs apart. Close your eyes and relax your body. Calm your mind.
2. Lean back, letting your weight rest on the stick—first on the left side of your back muscle and then on the right side. Repeat six to 24 times.

Warm up with *chi-shi*

1. *Be-mu*: Stand up, sit on a chair, or sit cross-legged on the floor with your eyes closed.
2. *Chang-tsuo*: Calm your mind.
3. *Tsuo-shou*: Put your palms together and rub them up and down until they feel warm.

4. *Bou-chee*: With your hands spread apart as if you were holding a big ball in front of you, inhale through your nose. Exhale through your mouth while bringing your hands back together.

Cool down with *shu-kon*

1. *Ko-chi*: Make a chewing motion with your mouth five to 100 times.
2. *Tu-na*: Sit on a chair or sit cross-legged on the floor with your eyes closed. Calm your mind. Inhale through your nose and hold your breath for two seconds. While you are holding your breath, imagine that *chi* is flowing from your brain and down your spinal cord and lower back. Exhale slowly through your mouth. When you breathe out, imagine that you are releasing the old *chi* from your body. When you breathe in, imagine that you are inhaling fresh *chi* from nature.

3. *Su-wien*: Wipe the inside of your mouth with your tongue three times. Keeping your tongue behind your upper front teeth, inhale through your mouth. Close your lips and move the air around with your lips and cheeks as if you were cleaning your mouth with it. Do this five to 10 times. If saliva begins to collect in your mouth while you are doing this, swallow it.
4. *Shi-yen*: As you inhale, put your index fingers on the *in-dou* pressure point and massage along your eyebrows until you reach the *tai-you* pressure points. Continue massaging your face until you reach the *hin-sha* pressure points and then massage your neck and chest as shown in the illustration. Repeat three times.

3. Crouch down on the floor and stretch your back. Breathing deeply, hold the stick with both hands and swing it back and forth on the ground, from left to right. Repeat 18 times.
4. Cool down with *shu-kon*.

3

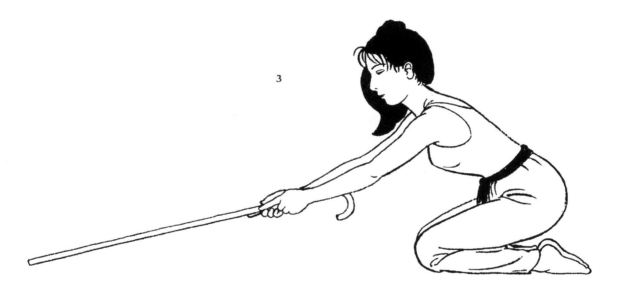

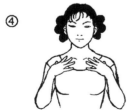

5. *Shu-to*: Close your eyes and put your index fingers on the *in-dou* pressure point. Massage your forehead and your scalp, moving down the back of your head, down your neck, and across your shoulders as shown in the illustration. Repeat three times.

6. *Shun-yo*: Sit on a chair and lift both of your arms up, back, and over your head with your wrists bent. Lift your feet off the floor and bend your toes. Inhale slowly and stretch your back. Then exhale while you bring your arms down to your sides and relax your entire body. Repeat twice.

Arthritis

1. For Stiff Knees: *Woo-rong-tan-jao*

1. In the cross-legged position, warm up with *chi-shi*.

2. Stretch your legs out in front of you and hold onto your toes. While pulling your toes up and toward your chest with your hands, try to push them down and away from your body as illustrated.

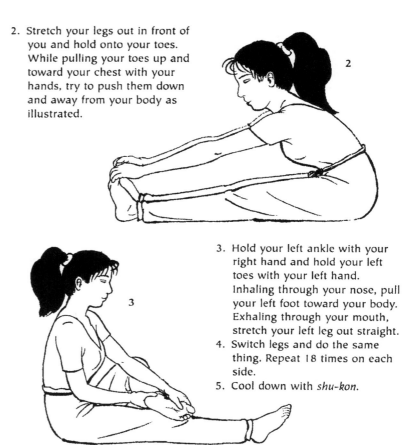

Warm up with *chi-shi*

1. *Be-mu*: Stand up, sit on a chair, or sit cross-legged on the floor with your eyes closed.
2. *Chang-tsuo*: Calm your mind.
3. *Tsuo-shou*: Put your palms together and rub them up and down until they feel warm.

4. *Bou-chee*: With your hands spread apart as if you were holding a big ball in front of you, inhale through your nose. Exhale through your mouth while bringing your hands back together.

3. Hold your left ankle with your right hand and hold your left toes with your left hand. Inhaling through your nose, pull your left foot toward your body. Exhaling through your mouth, stretch your left leg out straight.
4. Switch legs and do the same thing. Repeat 18 times on each side.
5. Cool down with *shu-kon*.

Cool down with *shu-kon*

1. *Ko-chi*: Make a chewing motion with your mouth five to 100 times.
2. *Tu-na*: Sit on a chair or sit cross-legged on the floor with your eyes closed. Calm your mind. Inhale through your nose and hold your breath for two seconds. While you are holding your breath, imagine that *chi* is flowing from your brain and down your spinal cord and lower back. Exhale slowly through your mouth. When you breathe out, imagine that you are releasing the old *chi* from your body. When you breathe in, imagine that you are inhaling fresh *chi* from nature.

3. *Su-wien*: Wipe the inside of your mouth with your tongue three times. Keeping your tongue behind your upper front teeth, inhale through your mouth. Close your lips and move the air around with your lips and cheeks as if you were cleaning your mouth with it. Do this five to 10 times. If saliva begins to collect in your mouth while you are doing this, swallow it.
4. *Shi-yen*: As you inhale, put your index fingers on the *in-dou* pressure point and massage along your eyebrows until you reach the *tai-you* pressure points. Continue massaging your face until you reach the *hin-sha* pressure points and then massage your neck and chest as shown in the illustration. Repeat three times.

2. For Arthritic Discomfort in the Knee and Hip Joints: *Ban-chan-to-shue*

1. In the standing position, warm up with *chi-shi*.
2. Put your right hand on the wall and your left hand on your hip as illustrated.
3. Lift your right knee. Keeping your right foot bent at a 90-degree angle, try to straighten your leg. Repeat six to 24 times.
4. Switch sides, putting your left hand on the wall and your right hand on your hip, and do the same thing with your left leg.
5. Cool down with *shu-kon*.

3

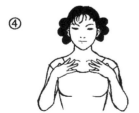

5. *Shu-to*: Close your eyes and put your index fingers on the *in-dou* pressure point. Massage your forehead and your scalp, moving down the back of your head, down your neck, and across your shoulders as shown in the illustration. Repeat three times.

6. *Shun-yo*: Sit on a chair and lift both of your arms up, back, and over your head with your wrists bent. Lift your feet off the floor and bend your toes. Inhale slowly and stretch your back. Then exhale while you bring your arms down to your sides and relax your entire body. Repeat twice.

Gout

I. For Shooting Pain in the Joints or Throughout the Entire Body: *Chin-ron-bai-jao*

1. In the cross-legged position, warm up with *chi-shi*.

2. Straighten your legs, clasp your hands together, and stretch your arms out in front of you. Rock your body from left to right 12 to 24 times.

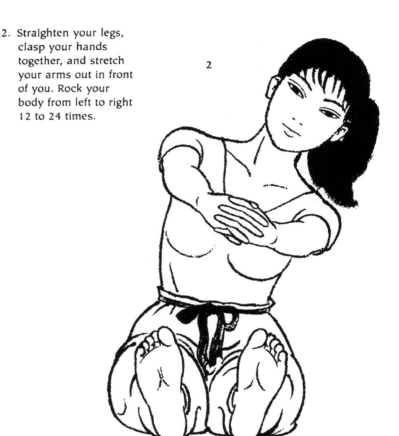

Warm up with *chi-shi*

1. *Be-mu:* Stand up, sit on a chair, or sit cross-legged on the floor with your eyes closed.
2. *Chang-tsuo:* Calm your mind.
3. *Tsuo-shou:* Put your palms together and rub them up and down until they feel warm.

4. *Bou-chee:* With your hands spread apart as if you were holding a big ball in front of you, inhale through your nose. Exhale through your mouth while bringing your hands back together.

Cool down with *shu-kon*

1. *Ko-chi:* Make a chewing motion with your mouth five to 100 times.
2. *Tu-na:* Sit on a chair or sit cross-legged on the floor with your eyes closed. Calm your mind. Inhale through your nose and hold your breath for two seconds. While you are holding your breath, imagine that *chi* is flowing from your brain and down your spinal cord and lower back. Exhale slowly through your mouth. When you breathe out, imagine that you are releasing the old *chi* from your body. When you breathe in, imagine that you are inhaling fresh *chi* from nature.

3. *Su-wien:* Wipe the inside of your mouth with your tongue three times. Keeping your tongue behind your upper front teeth, inhale through your mouth. Close your lips and move the air around with your lips and cheeks as if you were cleaning your mouth with it. Do this five to 10 times. If saliva begins to collect in your mouth while you are doing this, swallow it.
4. *Shi-yen:* As you inhale, put your index fingers on the *in-dou* pressure point and massage along your eyebrows until you reach the *tai-you* pressure points. Continue massaging your face until you reach the *hin-sha* pressure points and then massage your neck and chest as shown in the illustration. Repeat three times.

3. Bend your knees as illustrated, hold onto your big toes and rock back and forth 12 to 24 times.
4. Cool down with *shu-kon*.

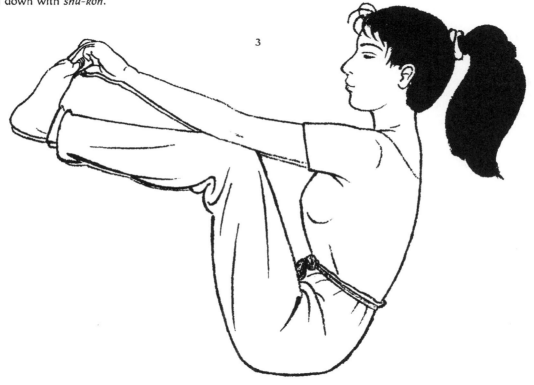

3

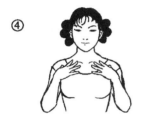

④

⑤

5. *Shu-to*: Close your eyes and put your index fingers on the *in-dou* pressure point. Massage your forehead and your scalp, moving down the back of your head, down your neck, and across your shoulders as shown in the illustration. Repeat three times.

⑥

6. *Shun-yo*: Sit on a chair and lift both of your arms up, back, and over your head with your wrists bent. Lift your feet off the floor and bend your toes. Inhale slowly and stretch your back. Then exhale while you bring your arms down to your sides and relax your entire body. Repeat twice.

2. For Severe Pain Due to Gout: *Bai-wei-san-ton*

1. In the standing position, warm up with *chi-shi*.

2. With your palms facing downward, move your hands from side to side. As you do this, step forward on your heel and imagine that you are ridding yourself of all your ills. When your hands swing left, look to the right. When your hands swing right, look to the left. Breathe naturally and walk this way for 20 to 100 steps.
3. Cool down with *shu-kon*.

Warm up with *chi-shi*

1. *Be-mu*: Stand up, sit on a chair, or sit cross-legged on the floor with your eyes closed.
2. *Chang-tsuo*: Calm your mind.
3. *Tsuo-shou*: Put your palms together and rub them up and down until they feel warm.

4. *Bou-chee*: With your hands spread apart as if you were holding a big ball in front of you, inhale through your nose. Exhale through your mouth while bringing your hands back together.

Cool down with *shu-kon*

1. *Ko-chi*: Make a chewing motion with your mouth five to 100 times.
2. *Tu-na*: Sit on a chair or sit cross-legged on the floor with your eyes closed. Calm your mind. Inhale through your nose and hold your breath for two seconds. While you are holding your breath, imagine that *chi* is flowing from your brain and down your spinal cord and lower back. Exhale slowly through your mouth. When you breathe out, imagine that you are releasing the old *chi* from your body. When you breathe in, imagine that you are inhaling fresh *chi* from nature.

3. *Su-wien*: Wipe the inside of your mouth with your tongue three times. Keeping your tongue behind your upper front teeth, inhale through your mouth. Close your lips and move the air around with your lips and cheeks as if you were cleaning your mouth with it. Do this five to 10 times. If saliva begins to collect in your mouth while you are doing this, swallow it.
4. *Shi-yen*: As you inhale, put your index fingers on the *in-dou* pressure point and massage along your eyebrows until you reach the *tai-you* pressure points. Continue massaging your face until you reach the *hin-sha* pressure points and then massage your neck and chest as shown in the illustration. Repeat three times.

Specific Breathing Techniques to Prevent and Treat Gynecological Disorders

Menstrual Problems

1. For Cramps: *Shao-nowan-tan-tien*

1. In the cross-legged position, warm up with *chi-shi*.
2. Cup your hands below your navel.
3. Inhale deeply through your nose and imagine that you are drawing your *chi* up through the *shimo-tan-da* pressure point. Exhale through your mouth. Repeat 20 to 40 times.
4. Cool down with *shu-kon*.

3

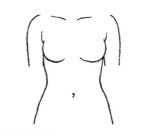

- *Ki-kai* is the pressure point located approximately one inch below your navel.
- *Shimo-tan-da* is the pressure point surrounding *ki-kai*.

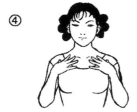

④

⑤

⑥

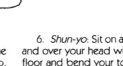

5. *Shu-to*: Close your eyes and put your index fingers on the *in-dou* pressure point. Massage your forehead and your scalp, moving down the back of your head, down your neck, and across your shoulders as shown in the illustration. Repeat three times.

6. *Shun-yo*: Sit on a chair and lift both of your arms up, back, and over your head with your wrists bent. Lift your feet off the floor and bend your toes. Inhale slowly and stretch your back. Then exhale while you bring your arms down to your sides and relax your entire body. Repeat twice.

2. For Dark-colored Menstrual Blood: *Woo-hoo-boo-shi*

1. In the cross-legged position, warm up with *chi-shi*.

2. Lie down on your stomach and lift your arms and legs above your back as illustrated. Move them back and forth. Repeat six to 24 times. If you can't comfortably get your arms into the position in the illustration, keep them on your head.

3. Return to the cross-legged position and hold your hands on your knees, palms up.

4. Cool down with *shu-kon*.

Warm up with *chi-shi*

1. *Be-mu*: Stand up, sit on a chair, or sit cross-legged on the floor with your eyes closed.
2. *Chang-tsuo*: Calm your mind.
3. *Tsuo-shou*: Put your palms together and rub them up and down until they feel warm.

4. *Bou-chee*: With your hands spread apart as if you were holding a big ball in front of you, inhale through your nose. Exhale through your mouth while bringing your hands back together.

2

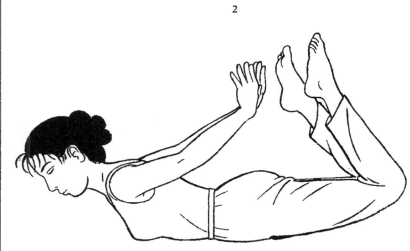

Cool down with *shu-kon*

1. *Ko-chi*: Make a chewing motion with your mouth five to 100 times.
2. *Tu-na*: Sit on a chair or sit cross-legged on the floor with your eyes closed. Calm your mind. Inhale through your nose and hold your breath for two seconds. While you are holding your breath, imagine that *chi* is flowing from your brain and down your spinal cord and lower back. Exhale slowly through your mouth. When you breathe out, imagine that you are releasing the old *chi* from your body. When you breathe in, imagine that you are inhaling fresh *chi* from nature.

3. *Su-wien*: Wipe the inside of your mouth with your tongue three times. Keeping your tongue behind your upper front teeth, inhale through your mouth. Close your lips and move the air around with your lips and cheeks as if you were cleaning your mouth with it. Do this five to 10 times. If saliva begins to collect in your mouth while you are doing this, swallow it.
4. *Shi-yen*: As you inhale, put your index fingers on the *in-dou* pressure point and massage along your eyebrows until you reach the *tai-you* pressure points. Continue massaging your face until you reach the *hin-sha* pressure points and then massage your neck and chest as shown in the illustration. Repeat three times.

3. For Cramps With Excessive Bleeding:
To-tien-an-dean

1. In the cross-legged position, warm up with *chi-shi*.
2. Clasp your hands together and stretch your arms toward the sky with your palms facing upward.
3. Exhale forcefully five times ("hoo-hoo-hoo-hoo-hoo").
4. As you exhale slowly, put your hands, palms down, on top of your head.
5. Exhale deeply and raise your arms, palms up, over your head.
6. Repeat steps 4 and 5 six to 12 times.
7. Cool down with *shu-kon*.

2, 3

4

5. *Shu-to*: Close your eyes and put your index fingers on the *in-dou* pressure point. Massage your forehead and your scalp, moving down the back of your head, down your neck, and across your shoulders as shown in the illustration. Repeat three times.

6. *Shun-yo*: Sit on a chair and lift both of your arms up, back, and over your head with your wrists bent. Lift your feet off the floor and bend your toes. Inhale slowly and stretch your back. Then exhale while you bring your arms down to your sides and relax your entire body. Repeat twice.

For Excessive Bleeding: *Tai-shi-yan-jan*

1. In a very quiet room, warm up with *chi-shi* while lying on your back.

2. Close your eyes. Very, very calmly inhale through your nose and exhale through your mouth.

3. Repeat step 2 about 300 times. We call this the "breathing technique for a sleeping baby" because it is so peaceful and quiet.

4. Cool down with *shu-kon*.

Warm up with *chi-shi*

1. *Be-mu*: Stand up, sit on a chair, or sit cross-legged on the floor with your eyes closed.

2. *Chang-tsuo*: Calm your mind.

3. *Tsuo-shou*: Put your palms together and rub them up and down until they feel warm.

4. *Bou-chee*: With your hands spread apart as if you were holding a big ball in front of you, inhale through your nose. Exhale through your mouth while bringing your hands back together.

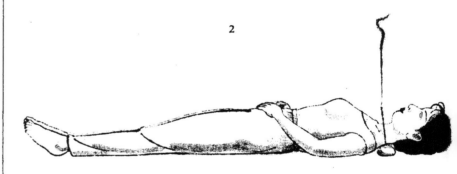

2

Cool down with *shu-kon*

1. *Ko-chi*: Make a chewing motion with your mouth five to 100 times.

2. *Tu-na*: Sit on a chair or sit cross-legged on the floor with your eyes closed. Calm your mind. Inhale through your nose and hold your breath for two seconds. While you are holding your breath, imagine that *chi* is flowing from your brain and down your spinal cord and lower back. Exhale slowly through your mouth. When you breathe out, imagine that you are releasing the old *chi* from your body. When you breathe in, imagine that you are inhaling fresh *chi* from nature.

3. *Su-wien*: Wipe the inside of your mouth with your tongue three times. Keeping your tongue behind your upper front teeth, inhale through your mouth. Close your lips and move the air around with your lips and cheeks as if you were cleaning your mouth with it. Do this five to 10 times. If saliva begins to collect in your mouth while you are doing this, swallow it.

4. *Shi-yen*: As you inhale, put your index fingers on the *in-dou* pressure point and massage along your eyebrows until you reach the *tai-you* pressure points. Continue massaging your face until you reach the *hin-sha* pressure points and then massage your neck and chest as shown in the illustration. Repeat three times.

For Cramps and Bloating:
Ree-bai-wan-yue

1. In the cross-legged position, warm up with *chi-shi*.
2. Holding onto your feet with your hands, take six to 12 steps, as illustrated. As you do this, keep your back stretched.
3. Crawling on your hands and knees like a cat, stretch your back. Repeat twice. Relax and lie face down on the ground. Cool down with *shu-kon*.

2

3

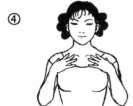

5. *Shu-to*: Close your eyes and put your index fingers on the *in-dou* pressure point. Massage your forehead and your scalp, moving down the back of your head, down your neck, and across your shoulders as shown in the illustration. Repeat three times.

6. *Shun-yo*: Sit on a chair and lift both of your arms up, back, and over your head with your wrists bent. Lift your feet off the floor and bend your toes. Inhale slowly and stretch your back. Then exhale while you bring your arms down to your sides and relax your entire body. Repeat twice.

For Female Infertility: *Shen-tan-shi-ran*

1. In the cross-legged position, warm up with *chi-shi*.

Warm up with *chi-shi*

1. *Be-mu*: Stand up, sit on a chair, or sit cross-legged on the floor with your eyes closed.
2. *Chang-tsuo*: Calm your mind.
3. *Tsuo-shou*: Put your palms together and rub them up and down until they feel warm.

4. *Bou-chee*: With your hands spread apart as if you were holding a big ball in front of you, inhale through your nose. Exhale through your mouth while bringing your hands back together.

---

2. Rub your back with your fists. As you move your hands up, inhale through your nose. As you move your hands down, exhale through your mouth. Repeat 24 times. (If your sexual partner rubs your back for you, this exercise is even more effective.)
3. Cool down with *shu-kon*.

Cool down with *shu-kon*

1. *Ko-chi*: Make a chewing motion with your mouth five to 100 times.
2. *Tu-na*: Sit on a chair or sit cross-legged on the floor with your eyes closed. Calm your mind. Inhale through your nose and hold your breath for two seconds. While you are holding your breath, imagine that *chi* is flowing from your brain and down your spinal cord and lower back. Exhale slowly through your mouth. When you breathe out, imagine that you are releasing the old *chi* from your body. When you breathe in, imagine that you are inhaling fresh *chi* from nature.

3. *Su-wien*: Wipe the inside of your mouth with your tongue three times. Keeping your tongue behind your upper front teeth, inhale through your mouth. Close your lips and move the air around with your lips and cheeks as if you were cleaning your mouth with it. Do this five to 10 times. If saliva begins to collect in your mouth while you are doing this, swallow it.
4. *Shi-yen*: As you inhale, put your index fingers on the *in-dou* pressure point and massage along your eyebrows until you reach the *tai-you* pressure points. Continue massaging your face until you reach the *hin-sha* pressure points and then massage your neck and chest as shown in the illustration. Repeat three times.

Menopause

1. For Anxiety or Nervousness Associated With Menopause: *Rin-niu-shin-bin*

1. In the standing position, warm up with *chi-shi*.
2. As you inhale through your nose, take one step forward with your right foot. At the same time, lift your right arm with your palm facing up and your thumb extended. Press the *nai-kan* pressure point on your right arm with your left thumb as illustrated.
3. As you exhale through your nose, switch your arms and legs and repeat step 2. Repeat 10 to 24 times on each side.
4. Cool down with *shu-kon*.

- *Nai-kan* is the pressure point located on the inside of your arm, approximately one inch above your wrist.

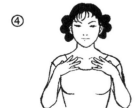

5. *Shu-to*: Close your eyes and put your index fingers on the *in-dou* pressure point. Massage your forehead and your scalp, moving down the back of your head, down your neck, and across your shoulders as shown in the illustration. Repeat three times.

6. *Shun-yo*: Sit on a chair and lift both of your arms up, back, and over your head with your wrists bent. Lift your feet off the floor and bend your toes. Inhale slowly and stretch your back. Then exhale while you bring your arms down to your sides and relax your entire body. Repeat twice.

2. For Insomnia or Night Sweats Associated With Menopause: *An-chi-wan-jo*

1. In the cross-legged position, warm up with *chi-shi*.

2. Press your left knee with your left hand and press your left elbow with your right hand. Maintain this position while breathing deeply 10 times.

3. Switch hands, pressing your right knee with your right hand and pressing your right elbow with your left hand. Repeat step 2.

4. Cool down with *shu-kon*.

2

Warm up with *chi-shi*

1. *Be-mu*: Stand up, sit on a chair, or sit cross-legged on the floor with your eyes closed.

2. *Chang-tsuo*: Calm your mind.

3. *Tsuo-shou*: Put your palms together and rub them up and down until they feel warm.

4. *Bou-chee*: With your hands spread apart as if you were holding a big ball in front of you, inhale through your nose. Exhale through your mouth while bringing your hands back together.

Cool down with *shu-kon*

1. *Ko-chi*: Make a chewing motion with your mouth five to 100 times.

2. *Tu-na*: Sit on a chair or sit cross-legged on the floor with your eyes closed. Calm your mind. Inhale through your nose and hold your breath for two seconds. While you are holding your breath, imagine that *chi* is flowing from your brain and down your spinal cord and lower back. Exhale slowly through your mouth. When you breathe out, imagine that you are releasing the old *chi* from your body. When you breathe in, imagine that you are inhaling fresh *chi* from nature.

3. *Su-wien*: Wipe the inside of your mouth with your tongue three times. Keeping your tongue behind your upper front teeth, inhale through your mouth. Close your lips and move the air around with your lips and cheeks as if you were cleaning your mouth with it. Do this five to 10 times. If saliva begins to collect in your mouth while you are doing this, swallow it.

4. *Shi-yen*: As you inhale, put your index fingers on the *in-dou* pressure point and massage along your eyebrows until you reach the *tai-you* pressure points. Continue massaging your face until you reach the *hin-sha* pressure points and then massage your neck and chest as shown in the illustration. Repeat three times.

3. For Fatigue Associated With Menopause:
Ban-yun-shi-jin

1. In the cross-legged position, warm up with *chi-shi*.
2. Stretch your legs out in front of you.
3. Grasp your toes and inhale deeply through your nose. While pulling your toes up and toward your chest with your hands, try to push them down and away from your body, as illustrated.
4. Exhale through your mouth and relax your body.
5. Repeat steps 3 and 4 six to 12 times.
6. Cool down with *shu-kon*.

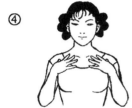

5. *Shu-to*: Close your eyes and put your index fingers on the *in-dou* pressure point. Massage your forehead and your scalp, moving down the back of your head, down your neck, and across your shoulders as shown in the illustration. Repeat three times.

6. *Shun-yo*: Sit on a chair and lift both of your arms up, back, and over your head with your wrists bent. Lift your feet off the floor and bend your toes. Inhale slowly and stretch your back. Then exhale while you bring your arms down to your sides and relax your entire body. Repeat twice.

Specific Breathing Techniques to Prevent and Treat Metabolic and Menopausal Disorders

Diabetes

1. For Weight Gain Caused by Overeating: *Ree-ju-zo-yo*

1. In the standing position, warm up with *chi-shi*.

2. Put your weight on one leg and inhale deeply through your nose. With both hands, try to draw your *chi* up and out.

3. Exhaling through your mouth, switch legs and do the same thing.

4. Repeat 12 to 24 times on each leg.

5. Cool down with *shu-kon*.

Warm up with *chi-shi*

1. *Be-mu*: Stand up, sit on a chair, or sit cross-legged on the floor with your eyes closed.

2. *Chang-tsuo*: Calm your mind.

3. *Tsuo-shou*: Put your palms together and rub them up and down until they feel warm.

4. *Bou-chee*: With your hands spread apart as if you were holding a big ball in front of you, inhale through your nose. Exhale through your mouth while bringing your hands back together.

2

3

Cool down with *shu-kon*

1. *Ko-chi*: Make a chewing motion with your mouth five to 100 times.

2. *Tu-na*: Sit on a chair or sit cross-legged on the floor with your eyes closed. Calm your mind. Inhale through your nose and hold your breath for two seconds. While you are holding your breath, imagine that *chi* is flowing from your brain and down your spinal cord and lower back. Exhale slowly through your mouth. When you breathe out, imagine that you are releasing the old *chi* from your body. When you breathe in, imagine that you are inhaling fresh *chi* from nature.

3. *Su-wien*: Wipe the inside of your mouth with your tongue three times. Keeping your tongue behind your upper front teeth, inhale through your mouth. Close your lips and move the air around with your lips and cheeks as if you were cleaning your mouth with it. Do this five to 10 times. If saliva begins to collect in your mouth while you are doing this, swallow it.

4. *Shi-yen*: As you inhale, put your index fingers on the *in-dou* pressure point and massage along your eyebrows until you reach the *tai-you* pressure points. Continue massaging your face until you reach the *hin-sha* pressure points and then massage your neck and chest as shown in the illustration. Repeat three times.

2. For Weight Loss: *Yan-ah-yao-shen*

1. In the cross-legged position, warm up with *chi-shi*.
2. Lead your *chi* up from your stomach to your head. Cover your ears with your hands and rock your upper body from left to right. Repeat 15 times.
3. Cool down with *shu-kon*.

2

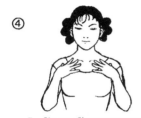

④

⑤

⑥

5. *Shu-to*: Close your eyes and put your index fingers on the *in-dou* pressure point. Massage your forehead and your scalp, moving down the back of your head, down your neck, and across your shoulders as shown in the illustration. Repeat three times.

6. *Shun-yo*: Sit on a chair and lift both of your arms up, back, and over your head with your wrists bent. Lift your feet off the floor and bend your toes. Inhale slowly and stretch your back. Then exhale while you bring your arms down to your sides and relax your entire body. Repeat twice.

Obesity

1. To Firm Up the Legs: *Yeu-chan-shi-jen-guon*

1. In the sitting position, warm up with *chi-shi*. With your feet flat on the floor, spread your knees slightly apart, keeping them bent at a 90-degree angle as illustrated.
2. Bend over and place your elbows on your knees. Clasp your hands together as if you were holding an egg and put your forehead on your hands.
3. Exhale through your mouth, emptying your lungs completely. Then inhale through your nose, pulling as much air as possible into your stomach.
4. Inhale very slowly and hold your breath for two seconds. Then exhale quickly.
5. Exhale through your nose. Repeat the exercise 20 times.
6. Cool down with the *shi-yen*, *shu-to*, and *shun-yo* steps of *shu-kon*.

Warm up with *chi-shi*

1. *Be-mu*: Stand up, sit on a chair, or sit cross-legged on the floor with your eyes closed.
2. *Chang-tsuo*: Calm your mind.
3. *Tsuo-shou*: Put your palms together and rub them up and down until they feel warm.

4. *Bou-chee*: With your hands spread apart as if you were holding a big ball in front of you, inhale through your nose. Exhale through your mouth while bringing your hands back together.

3, 4

Cool down with *shu-kon*

1. *Ko-chi*: Make a chewing motion with your mouth five to 100 times.
2. *Tu-na*: Sit on a chair or sit cross-legged on the floor with your eyes closed. Calm your mind. Inhale through your nose and hold your breath for two seconds. While you are holding your breath, imagine that *chi* is flowing from your brain and down your spinal cord and lower back. Exhale slowly through your mouth. When you breathe out, imagine that you are releasing the old *chi* from your body. When you breathe in, imagine that you are inhaling fresh *chi* from nature.

3. *Su-wien*: Wipe the inside of your mouth with your tongue three times. Keeping your tongue behind your upper front teeth, inhale through your mouth. Close your lips and move the air around with your lips and cheeks as if you were cleaning your mouth with it. Do this five to 10 times. If saliva begins to collect in your mouth while you are doing this, swallow it.
4. *Shi-yen*: As you inhale, put your index fingers on the *in-dou* pressure point and massage along your eyebrows until you reach the *tai-you* pressure points. Continue massaging your face until you reach the *hin-sha* pressure points and then massage your neck and chest as shown in the illustration. Repeat three times.

2. To Curb the Appetite: *Rien-fowa-guon*

1. Sitting in a chair, either in the cross-legged position or with your feet on the ground and your legs slightly apart, warm up with *chi-shi*. Place your hands on your knees, palms up, and breathe deeply.
2. Breathe naturally. Clear your mind by focusing on your breathing.
3. Inhale naturally and exhale as if you were blowing the air out. You will be able to hear your breath. Continue for five minutes.
4. Breathe naturally for five minutes and then cool down with *shu-kon*.

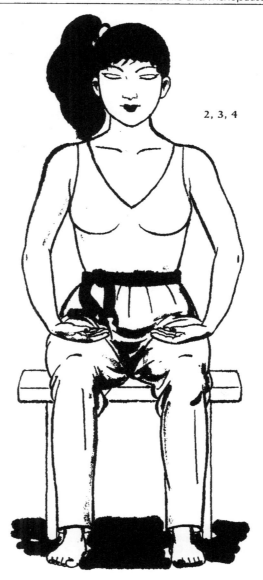

2, 3, 4

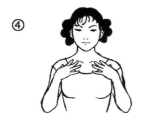

5. *Shu-to*: Close your eyes and put your index fingers on the *in-dou* pressure point. Massage your forehead and your scalp, moving down the back of your head, down your neck, and across your shoulders as shown in the illustration. Repeat three times.

6. *Shun-yo*: Sit on a chair and lift both of your arms up, back, and over your head with your wrists bent. Lift your feet off the floor and bend your toes. Inhale slowly and stretch your back. Then exhale while you bring your arms down to your sides and relax your entire body. Repeat twice.

3. To Firm Up the Stomach: *Lu-chan-fan-ran-guon*

1. Sitting in a chair, either in the cross-legged position or with your feet on the ground and your legs slightly apart, warm up with *chi-shi*. Relax your entire body. If you are a man, place your right hand on your chest and your left hand under your stomach. If you are a woman, place your left hand on your chest and your right hand under your stomach.

2. Push out your chest and pull in your stomach as you inhale. Pull in your chest and push out your stomach as you exhale. Do this breathing exercise about 30 minutes before each meal, 20 to 60 times. You can breathe either through your nose or through your mouth. If breathing through your nose, close your mouth slightly and keep your tongue behind your front teeth.

3. Cool down with the *shi-yen*, *shu-to*, and *shun-yo* steps of *shu-kon*.

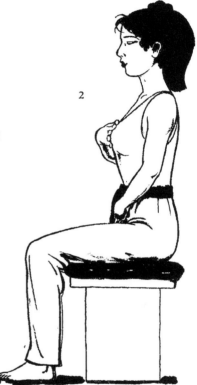

2

Warm up with *chi-shi*

1. *Be-mu*: Stand up, sit on a chair, or sit cross-legged on the floor with your eyes closed.
2. *Chang-tsuo*: Calm your mind.
3. *Tsuo-shou*: Put your palms together and rub them up and down until they feel warm.

4. *Bou-chee*: With your hands spread apart as if you were holding a big ball in front of you, inhale through your nose. Exhale through your mouth while bringing your hands back together.

Cool down with *shu-kon*

1. *Ko-chi*: Make a chewing motion with your mouth five to 100 times.
2. *Tu-na*: Sit on a chair or sit cross-legged on the floor with your eyes closed. Calm your mind. Inhale through your nose and hold your breath for two seconds. While you are holding your breath, imagine that *chi* is flowing from your brain and down your spinal cord and lower back. Exhale slowly through your mouth. When you breathe out, imagine that you are releasing the old *chi* from your body. When you breathe in, imagine that you are inhaling fresh *chi* from nature.

3. *Su-wien*: Wipe the inside of your mouth with your tongue three times. Keeping your tongue behind your upper front teeth, inhale through your mouth. Close your lips and move the air around with your lips and cheeks as if you were cleaning your mouth with it. Do this five to 10 times. If saliva begins to collect in your mouth while you are doing this, swallow it.
4. *Shi-yen*: As you inhale, put your index fingers on the *in-dou* pressure point and massage along your eyebrows until you reach the *tai-you* pressure points. Continue massaging your face until you reach the *hin-sha* pressure points and then massage your neck and chest as shown in the illustration. Repeat three times.

Anorexia

1. For Digestive Problems: *Shao-nowan-tan-tien*

1. In the cross-legged position, warm up with *chi-shi*.
2. Cup your hands under your navel, in front of your *ki-kai* pressure point.
3. Inhaling deeply through your nose, guide your *chi* down to your *shimo-tan-da* pressure point and exhale through your mouth. Repeat 20 to 40 times.

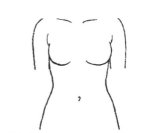

- *Ki-kai* is the pressure point located approximately one inch below your navel.
- *Shimo-tan-da* is the pressure point surrounding *ki-kai*.

 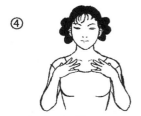 

5. *Shu-to*: Close your eyes and put your index fingers on the *in-dou* pressure point. Massage your forehead and your scalp, moving down the back of your head, down your neck, and across your shoulders as shown in the illustration. Repeat three times.

6. *Shun-yo*: Sit on a chair and lift both of your arms up, back, and over your head with your wrists bent. Lift your feet off the floor and bend your toes. Inhale slowly and stretch your back. Then exhale while you bring your arms down to your sides and relax your entire body. Repeat twice.

2. For Loss of Appetite: *To-teien-an-ji*

1. In the cross-legged position, warm up with *chi-shi*.

2. Hold the toes of your left foot with your left hand as illustrated and inhale through your nose. Push your right hand up to the sky. Look at your right hand.
3. Exhaling through your mouth, switch hands and do the same thing.
4. Repeat 12 to 24 times steps 2 and 3.
5. Cool down with *shu-kon*.

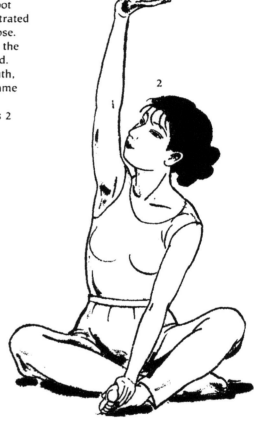

Warm up with *chi-shi*

1. *Be-mu*: Stand up, sit on a chair, or sit cross-legged on the floor with your eyes closed.
2. *Chang-tsuo*: Calm your mind.
3. *Tsuo-shou*: Put your palms together and rub them up and down until they feel warm.

4. *Bou-chee*: With your hands spread apart as if you were holding a big ball in front of you, inhale through your nose. Exhale through your mouth while bringing your hands back together.

Cool down with *shu-kon*

1. *Ko-chi*: Make a chewing motion with your mouth five to 100 times.
2. *Tu-na*: Sit on a chair or sit cross-legged on the floor with your eyes closed. Calm your mind. Inhale through your nose and hold your breath for two seconds. While you are holding your breath, imagine that *chi* is flowing from your brain and down your spinal cord and lower back. Exhale slowly through your mouth. When you breathe out, imagine that you are releasing the old *chi* from your body. When you breathe in, imagine that you are inhaling fresh *chi* from nature.

3. *Su-wien*: Wipe the inside of your mouth with your tongue three times. Keeping your tongue behind your upper front teeth, inhale through your mouth. Close your lips and move the air around with your lips and cheeks as if you were cleaning your mouth with it. Do this five to 10 times. If saliva begins to collect in your mouth while you are doing this, swallow it.
4. *Shi-yen*: As you inhale, put your index fingers on the *in-dou* pressure point and massage along your eyebrows until you reach the *tai-you* pressure points. Continue massaging your face until you reach the *hin-sha* pressure points and then massage your neck and chest as shown in the illustration. Repeat three times.

Sensitivity to Cold

1. For Cold Feet: *Shin-pi-tei-ji*

1. In the standing position, warm up with *chi-shi*.
2. As you step forward with your right foot, transfer your weight to that foot as you bring your hands forward, palms up.
3. Pause, breathe deeply, and move your arms and legs as illustrated six to 12 times.
4. Step forward with your left foot and do the same thing.
5. Cool down with *shu-kon*.

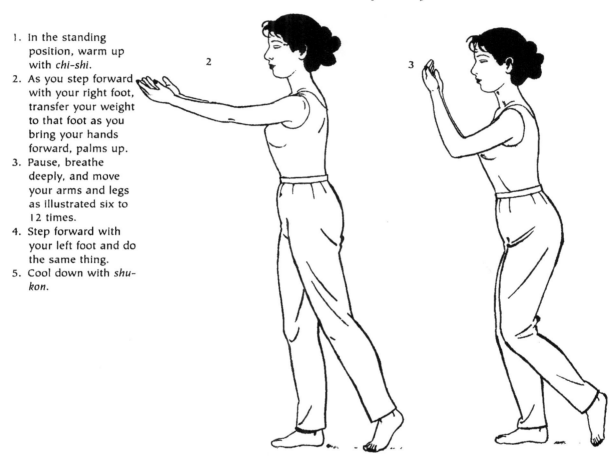

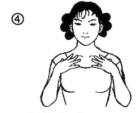

5. *Shu-to*: Close your eyes and put your index fingers on the *in-dou* pressure point. Massage your forehead and your scalp, moving down the back of your head, down your neck, and across your shoulders as shown in the illustration. Repeat three times.

6. *Shun-yo*: Sit on a chair and lift both of your arms up, back, and over your head with your wrists bent. Lift your feet off the floor and bend your toes. Inhale slowly and stretch your back. Then exhale while you bring your arms down to your sides and relax your entire body. Repeat twice.

2. For Pain in the Back, Hands, and Feet
When Exposed to Cold: *Shuan-pee-yao-ru*

1. In the cross-legged position, warm up with *chi-shi*.

2. Hold your hands behind your back. As you inhale through your nose, bring your shoulders forward, imagining that you are drawing *chi* down toward your heels. As you exhale, move your shoulders back, imagining that you are drawing *chi* up toward your head. Repeat six to 36 times.

3. Cool down with *shu-kon*.

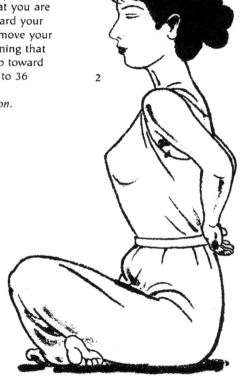

Warm up with *chi-shi*

1. *Be-mu*: Stand up, sit on a chair, or sit cross-legged on the floor with your eyes closed.
2. *Chang-tsuo*: Calm your mind.
3. *Tsuo-shou*: Put your palms together and rub them up and down until they feel warm.

4. *Bou-chee*: With your hands spread apart as if you were holding a big ball in front of you, inhale through your nose. Exhale through your mouth while bringing your hands back together.

Cool down with *shu-kon*

1. *Ko-chi*: Make a chewing motion with your mouth five to 100 times.
2. *Tu-na*: Sit on a chair or sit cross-legged on the floor with your eyes closed. Calm your mind. Inhale through your nose and hold your breath for two seconds. While you are holding your breath, imagine that *chi* is flowing from your brain and down your spinal cord and lower back. Exhale slowly through your mouth. When you breathe out, imagine that you are releasing the old *chi* from your body. When you breathe in, imagine that you are inhaling fresh *chi* from nature.

3. *Su-wien*: Wipe the inside of your mouth with your tongue three times. Keeping your tongue behind your upper front teeth, inhale through your mouth. Close your lips and move the air around with your lips and cheeks as if you were cleaning your mouth with it. Do this five to 10 times. If saliva begins to collect in your mouth while you are doing this, swallow it.
4. *Shi-yen*: As you inhale, put your index fingers on the *in-dou* pressure point and massage along your eyebrows until you reach the *tai-you* pressure points. Continue massaging your face until you reach the *hin-sha* pressure points and then massage your neck and chest as shown in the illustration. Repeat three times.

Emotional Pain

1. For Anger or Agitation: *To-teien-dao-jang*

1. In the standing position, warm up with *chi-shi*.
2. Hold your hands in front of your eyes and move them in a circle, clockwise, to draw *chi* into your eyes. Then move your hands to your stomach to draw the *chi* there.
3. Move your left leg forward. As you inhale, raise your hands (palms up) high over your head and imagine that you are releasing the *chi* on your palms into the air.

2

3

5. *Shu-to*: Close your eyes and put your index fingers on the *in-dou* pressure point. Massage your forehead and your scalp, moving down the back of your head, down your neck, and across your shoulders as shown in the illustration. Repeat three times.

6. *Shun-yo*: Sit on a chair and lift both of your arms up, back, and over your head with your wrists bent. Lift your feet off the floor and bend your toes. Inhale slowly and stretch your back. Then exhale while you bring your arms down to your sides and relax your entire body. Repeat twice.

4. As you exhale, bring your palms down toward your stomach, imagining that you are drawing new *chi* into your body.
5. Move your right leg forward and repeat step 3.
6. Repeat steps 3 through 5 slowly and rhythmically, taking nine steps forward with each leg.
7. Cool down with the *shun-yo* step of *shu-kon*.

Warm up with *chi-shi*

1. *Be-mu*: Stand up, sit on a chair, or sit cross-legged on the floor with your eyes closed.
2. *Chang-tsuo*: Calm your mind.
3. *Tsuo-shou*: Put your palms together and rub them up and down until they feel warm.

4. *Bou-chee*: With your hands spread apart as if you were holding a big ball in front of you, inhale through your nose. Exhale through your mouth while bringing your hands back together.

Cool down with *shu-kon*

1. *Ko-chi*: Make a chewing motion with your mouth five to 100 times.
2. *Tu-na*: Sit on a chair or sit cross-legged on the floor with your eyes closed. Calm your mind. Inhale through your nose and hold your breath for two seconds. While you are holding your breath, imagine that *chi* is flowing from your brain and down your spinal cord and lower back. Exhale slowly through your mouth. When you breathe out, imagine that you are releasing the old *chi* from your body. When you breathe in, imagine that you are inhaling fresh *chi* from nature.

3. *Su-wien*: Wipe the inside of your mouth with your tongue three times. Keeping your tongue behind your upper front teeth, inhale through your mouth. Close your lips and move the air around with your lips and cheeks as if you were cleaning your mouth with it. Do this five to 10 times. If saliva begins to collect in your mouth while you are doing this, swallow it.
4. *Shi-yen*: As you inhale, put your index fingers on the *in-dou* pressure point and massage along your eyebrows until you reach the *tai-you* pressure points. Continue massaging your face until you reach the *hin-sha* pressure points and then massage your neck and chest as shown in the illustration. Repeat three times.

2. For Fatigue: *Jo-tie-nho-hao*

1. In the cross-legged position, warm up with *chi-shi*.
2. Pull up on the sides of your stomach with your hands. As you inhale, imagine that you are also pulling up your groin.
3. Exhale and relax your hands and body.
4. Repeat 12 to 24 times steps 2 and 3.
5. Cool down with *shu-kon*.

2

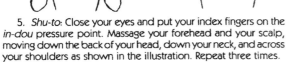

5. *Shu-to:* Close your eyes and put your index fingers on the *in-dou* pressure point. Massage your forehead and your scalp, moving down the back of your head, down your neck, and across your shoulders as shown in the illustration. Repeat three times.

6. *Shun-yo:* Sit on a chair and lift both of your arms up, back, and over your head with your wrists bent. Lift your feet off the floor and bend your toes. Inhale slowly and stretch your back. Then exhale while you bring your arms down to your sides and relax your entire body. Repeat twice.

Heart Problems

1. For Fast Heartbeat: *To-tien-ta-de*

1. In the standing position, warm up with *chi-shi*.

Warm up with *chi-shi*

1. *Be-mu*: Stand up, sit on a chair, or sit cross-legged on the floor with your eyes closed.
2. *Chang-tsuo*: Calm your mind.
3. *Tsuo-shou*: Put your palms together and rub them up and down until they feel warm.

4. *Bou-chee*: With your hands spread apart as if you were holding a big ball in front of you, inhale through your nose. Exhale through your mouth while bringing your hands back together.

Cool down with *shu-kon*

1. *Ko-chi*: Make a chewing motion with your mouth five to 100 times.
2. *Tu-na*: Sit on a chair or sit cross-legged on the floor with your eyes closed. Calm your mind. Inhale through your nose and hold your breath for two seconds. While you are holding your breath, imagine that *chi* is flowing from your brain and down your spinal cord and lower back. Exhale slowly through your mouth. When you breathe out, imagine that you are releasing the old *chi* from your body. When you breathe in, imagine that you are inhaling fresh *chi* from nature.

3. *Su-wien*: Wipe the inside of your mouth with your tongue three times. Keeping your tongue behind your upper front teeth, inhale through your mouth. Close your lips and move the air around with your lips and cheeks as if you were cleaning your mouth with it. Do this five to 10 times. If saliva begins to collect in your mouth while you are doing this, swallow it.
4. *Shi-yen*: As you inhale, put your index fingers on the *in-dou* pressure point and massage along your eyebrows until you reach the *tai-you* pressure points. Continue massaging your face until you reach the *hin-sha* pressure points and then massage your neck and chest as shown in the illustration. Repeat three times.

2. Stand with your hands apart and your knees bent.
3. Breathe deeply and stand up straight, releasing *chi* to the sky with your palms up. Breathe deeply and step to your right and left 24 to 35 times.
4. Cool down with *shu-kon*.

2. For Low Blood Pressure and a Slow Heartbeat: *Shan-pao-tan-tien*

1. In the standing position, warm up with *chi-shi*.
2. Cup your hands in front of your *ki-kai* pressure point as if you were carrying something.
3. Bend your knees up and down. As you move down, exhale through your mouth. As you move up, inhale through your nose. Repeat 50 to 200 times.
4. Cool down with *shu-kon*.

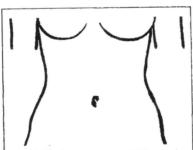

- *Ki-kai* is the pressure point located approximately one inch below your navel.

5. *Shu-to*: Close your eyes and put your index fingers on the *in-dou* pressure point. Massage your forehead and your scalp, moving down the back of your head, down your neck, and across your shoulders as shown in the illustration. Repeat three times.

6. *Shun-yo*: Sit on a chair and lift both of your arms up, back, and over your head with your wrists bent. Lift your feet off the floor and bend your toes. Inhale slowly and stretch your back. Then exhale while you bring your arms down to your sides and relax your entire body. Repeat twice.

For Sweating: *So-tei-zon-shen*

1. In the cross-legged position, warm up with *chi-shi*.

2. Place your hands on the ground in front of you and inhale through your mouth as you bend over. Hold your breath for two seconds.

Warm up with *chi-shi*

1. *Be-mu*: Stand up, sit on a chair, or sit cross-legged on the floor with your eyes closed.
2. *Chang-tsuo*: Calm your mind.
3. *Tsuo-shou*: Put your palms together and rub them up and down until they feel warm.

4. *Bou-chee*: With your hands spread apart as if you were holding a big ball in front of you, inhale through your nose. Exhale through your mouth while bringing your hands back together.

3. Without moving your hands, lift your head as illustrated while inhaling through your nose.
4. Repeat steps 2 and 3 six to 12 times.
5. Cool down with *shu-kon*.

Cool down with *shu-kon*

1. *Ko-chi*: Make a chewing motion with your mouth five to 100 times.
2. *Tu-na*: Sit on a chair or sit cross-legged on the floor with your eyes closed. Calm your mind. Inhale through your nose and hold your breath for two seconds. While you are holding your breath, imagine that *chi* is flowing from your brain and down your spinal cord and lower back. Exhale slowly through your mouth. When you breathe out, imagine that you are releasing the old *chi* from your body. When you breathe in, imagine that you are inhaling fresh *chi* from nature.

3. *Su-wien*: Wipe the inside of your mouth with your tongue three times. Keeping your tongue behind your upper front teeth, inhale through your mouth. Close your lips and move the air around with your lips and cheeks as if you were cleaning your mouth with it. Do this five to 10 times. If saliva begins to collect in your mouth while you are doing this, swallow it.
4. *Shi-yen*: As you inhale, put your index fingers on the *in-dou* pressure point and massage along your eyebrows until you reach the *tai-you* pressure points. Continue massaging your face until you reach the *hin-sha* pressure points and then massage your neck and chest as shown in the illustration. Repeat three times.

For Gas: *To-tien-an-din*

1. In the cross-legged position, warm up with *chi-shi*.
2. Clasp your hands and extend your hands over your head, palms toward the sky.
3. Exhale forcefully through your mouth ("hoo-hoo-hoo-hoo-hoo").
4. As you exhale, slowly bring your hands back to your head, palms down.
5. Exhale forcefully once, and extend your hands over your head, palms toward the sky.
6. Repeat steps 4 and 5 six to 12 times.
7. Cool down with *shu-kon*.

2, 3

4

④

⑤

5. *Shu-to*: Close your eyes and put your index fingers on the *in-dou* pressure point. Massage your forehead and your scalp, moving down the back of your head, down your neck, and across your shoulders as shown in the illustration. Repeat three times.

⑥

6. *Shun-yo*: Sit on a chair and lift both of your arms up, back, and over your head with your wrists bent. Lift your feet off the floor and bend your toes. Inhale slowly and stretch your back. Then exhale while you bring your arms down to your sides and relax your entire body. Repeat twice.

Specific Breathing Techniques to Prevent and Treat Skin and Hair Disorders

For Eczema: *Yao-tien-jun*

1. In the cross-legged position, warm up with *chi-shi*.

2. Sit upright and cup your hands under your *chu-in* pressure point.

Warm up with *chi-shi*

1. *Be-mu*: Stand up, sit on a chair, or sit cross-legged on the floor with your eyes closed.
2. *Chang-tsuo*: Calm your mind.
3. *Tsuo-shou*: Put your palms together and rub them up and down until they feel warm.

4. *Bou-chee*: With your hands spread apart as if you were holding a big ball in front of you, inhale through your nose. Exhale through your mouth while bringing your hands back together.

2, 3

- *Chu-in* is the pressure point midway between your navel and the pit of your stomach.

3. Rock your body from right to left 12 to 24 times. Inhale through your nose and exhale through your mouth. Without whistling, blow the air out while keeping your tongue behind your front teeth.
4. Cool down with *shu-kon*.

Cool down with *shu-kon*

1. *Ko-chi*: Make a chewing motion with your mouth five to 100 times.
2. *Tu-na*: Sit on a chair or sit cross-legged on the floor with your eyes closed. Calm your mind. Inhale through your nose and hold your breath for two seconds. While you are holding your breath, imagine that *chi* is flowing from your brain and down your spinal cord and lower back. Exhale slowly through your mouth. When you breathe out, imagine that you are releasing the old *chi* from your body. When you breathe in, imagine that you are inhaling fresh *chi* from nature.

3. *Su-wien*: Wipe the inside of your mouth with your tongue three times. Keeping your tongue behind your upper front teeth, inhale through your mouth. Close your lips and move the air around with your lips and cheeks as if you were cleaning your mouth with it. Do this five to 10 times. If saliva begins to collect in your mouth while you are doing this, swallow it.
4. *Shi-yen*: As you inhale, put your index fingers on the *in-dou* pressure point and massage along your eyebrows until you reach the *tai-you* pressure points. Continue massaging your face until you reach the *hin-sha* pressure points and then massage your neck and chest as shown in the illustration. Repeat three times.

* *Hya-kkai* is the pressure point located on top of your head, midway between your two earlobes.

For Seborrhea: *An-pao-din-men*

1. In the cross-legged position, warm up with *chi-shi*.
2. Close your eyes and rest your clasped hands on your forehead. Inhale through your nose, imagining that *chi* is flowing through your brain.
3. As you exhale, extend your arms above your head and imagine that chi is flowing out of your brain through the *hya-kkai* pressure point.
4. Repeat 12 to 17 times steps 2 and 3.

5. Place your hands on your knees, palms up, and begin to cool down with *shu-kon*. Begin with the *ko-chi* step, making the chewing motion with your mouth 20 to 30 times. Then swallow your spit and repeat the *shun-yo* step twice.

5. *Shu-to:* Close your eyes and put your index fingers on the *in-dou* pressure point. Massage your forehead and your scalp, moving down the back of your head, down your neck, and across your shoulders as shown in the illustration. Repeat three times.

6. *Shun-yo:* Sit on a chair and lift both of your arms up, back, and over your head with your wrists bent. Lift your feet off the floor and bend your toes. Inhale slowly and stretch your back. Then exhale while you bring your arms down to your sides and relax your entire body. Repeat twice.

For Hair Loss: *Bai-yuan-shen-go*

1. In the standing position, warm up with *chi-shi*. If your age or physical conditon makes it difficult for you to warm up in the standing position, do it while seated in a chair.

Warm up with *chi-shi*

1. *Be-mu*: Stand up, sit on a chair, or sit cross-legged on the floor with your eyes closed.
2. *Chang-tsuo*: Calm your mind.
3. *Tsuo-shou*: Put your palms together and rub them up and down until they feel warm.

4. *Bou-chee*: With your hands spread apart as if you were holding a big ball in front of you, inhale through your nose. Exhale through your mouth while bringing your hands back together.

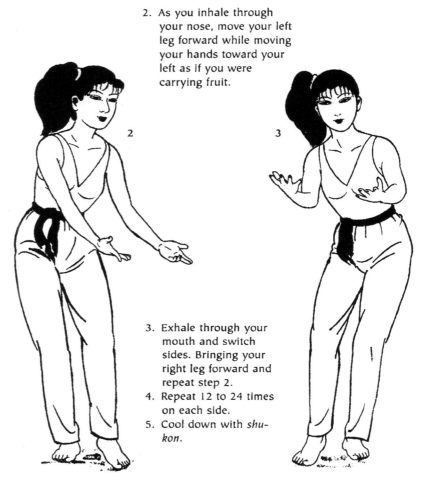

2. As you inhale through your nose, move your left leg forward while moving your hands toward your left as if you were carrying fruit.

3. Exhale through your mouth and switch sides. Bringing your right leg forward and repeat step 2.
4. Repeat 12 to 24 times on each side.
5. Cool down with *shu-kon*.

Cool down with *shu-kon*

1. *Ko-chi*: Make a chewing motion with your mouth five to 100 times.
2. *Tu-na*: Sit on a chair or sit cross-legged on the floor with your eyes closed. Calm your mind. Inhale through your nose and hold your breath for two seconds. While you are holding your breath, imagine that *chi* is flowing from your brain and down your spinal cord and lower back. Exhale slowly through your mouth. When you breathe out, imagine that you are releasing the old *chi* from your body. When you breathe in, imagine that you are inhaling fresh *chi* from nature.

3. *Su-wien*: Wipe the inside of your mouth with your tongue three times. Keeping your tongue behind your upper front teeth, inhale through your mouth. Close your lips and move the air around with your lips and cheeks as if you were cleaning your mouth with it. Do this five to 10 times. If saliva begins to collect in your mouth while you are doing this, swallow it.
4. *Shi-yen*: As you inhale, put your index fingers on the *in-dou* pressure point and massage along your eyebrows until you reach the *tai-you* pressure points. Continue massaging your face until you reach the *hin-sha* pressure points and then massage your neck and chest as shown in the illustration. Repeat three times.

Graying Hair

1. To Diminish Wrinkles and Darken Graying Hair: *Zo-di-dien*

1. In the cross-legged position, warm up with *chi-shi*.
2. Stretch your legs out in front of you and put your hands on your ankles. Press your *san-in-kou* pressure points with your thumbs while keeping your index fingers on your shins.
3. Bending your body down as far as possible, exhale slowly through your mouth.
4. As you inhale deeply through your nose, bring your back up to the sitting position.
5. Repeat steps 3 and 4 six to 12 times.
6. Cool down with *shu-kon*.

2, 3

- *San-in-kou* are the pressure points 5 inches above your ankle bone.

5. *Shu-to:* Close your eyes and put your index fingers on the *in-dou* pressure point. Massage your forehead and your scalp, moving down the back of your head, down your neck, and across your shoulders as shown in the illustration. Repeat three times.

6. *Shun-yo:* Sit on a chair and lift both of your arms up, back, and over your head with your wrists bent. Lift your feet off the floor and bend your toes. Inhale slowly and stretch your back. Then exhale while you bring your arms down to your sides and relax your entire body. Repeat twice.

2. To Brighten the Eyes and Darken Graying Hair: *Dun-ju-ju-ji*

1. In the standing position, warm up with *chi-shi*.

2. Bend over and grasp your toes with your hands. Inhale through your nose, keeping your head as far down between your legs as possible, as illustrated.

3. Without moving your body, exhale through your mouth.

4. As you inhale, bring your body back up to the sitting position.

5. Repeat steps 2 through 4 six to 12 times.

6. Cool down with *shu-kon*.

Warm up with *chi-shi*

1. *Be-mu*: Stand up, sit on a chair, or sit cross-legged on the floor with your eyes closed.

2. *Chang-tsuo*: Calm your mind.

3. *Tsuo-shou*: Put your palms together and rub them up and down until they feel warm.

4. *Bou-chee*: With your hands spread apart as if you were holding a big ball in front of you, inhale through your nose. Exhale through your mouth while bringing your hands back together.

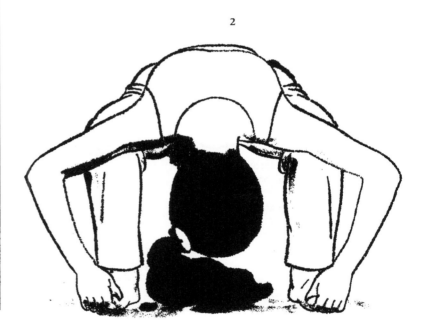

2

Cool down with *shu-kon*

1. *Ko-chi*: Make a chewing motion with your mouth five to 100 times.

2. *Tu-na*: Sit on a chair or sit cross-legged on the floor with your eyes closed. Calm your mind. Inhale through your nose and hold your breath for two seconds. While you are holding your breath, imagine that *chi* is flowing from your brain and down your spinal cord and lower back. Exhale slowly through your mouth. When you breathe out, imagine that you are releasing the old *chi* from your body. When you breathe in, imagine that you are inhaling fresh *chi* from nature.

3. *Su-wien*: Wipe the inside of your mouth with your tongue three times. Keeping your tongue behind your upper front teeth, inhale through your mouth. Close your lips and move the air around with your lips and cheeks as if you were cleaning your mouth with it. Do this five to 10 times. If saliva begins to collect in your mouth while you are doing this, swallow it.

4. *Shi-yen*: As you inhale, put your index fingers on the *in-dou* pressure point and massage along your eyebrows until you reach the *tai-you* pressure points. Continue massaging your face until you reach the *hin-sha* pressure points and then massage your neck and chest as shown in the illustration. Repeat three times.

Specific Breathing Techniques to Prevent and Treat Eye, Ear, Nose, and Throat Disorders

For Cataracts: *Yen-guwan-tai-ji*

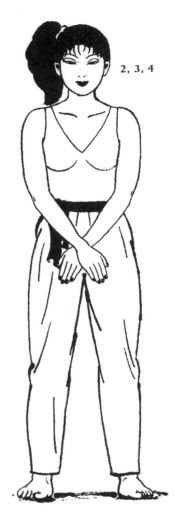

2, 3, 4

1. In the standing position, warm up with *chi-shi*.
2. Spread your legs apart and cross your wrists, keeping your right hand on top of your left.
3. Keeping your tongue behind your upper front teeth, try to focus your eyes on the tip of your nose while inhaling deeply through your nose.
4. As you inhale, imagine that you are moving *chi* down to your *yu-sen* pressure point. As you exhale, imagine that you are bringing the *chi* back up and blowing it out of your mouth. Breathe very quietly and gently.
5. Repeat steps 3 and 4 six to 36 times.
6. Cool down with *shu-kon*.

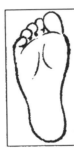

- *Yu-sen* is the pressure point a little above the center of the sole of your foot. If you bend your toes, you will see the hollow that forms around it.

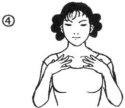

④ ⑤

5. *Shu-to*: Close your eyes and put your index fingers on the *in-dou* pressure point. Massage your forehead and your scalp, moving down the back of your head, down your neck, and across your shoulders as shown in the illustration. Repeat three times.

⑥

6. *Shun-yo*: Sit on a chair and lift both of your arms up, back, and over your head with your wrists bent. Lift your feet off the floor and bend your toes. Inhale slowly and stretch your back. Then exhale while you bring your arms down to your sides and relax your entire body. Repeat twice.

For Eyestrain: *In-tan-ba-zu-gon*

1. In the sitting position, warm up with *chi-shi*.

Warm up with *chi-shi*

1. *Be-mu*: Stand up, sit on a chair, or sit cross-legged on the floor with your eyes closed.
2. *Chang-tsuo*: Calm your mind.
3. *Tsuo-shou*: Put your palms together and rub them up and down until they feel warm.

4. *Bou-chee*: With your hands spread apart as if you were holding a big ball in front of you, inhale through your nose. Exhale through your mouth while bringing your hands back together.

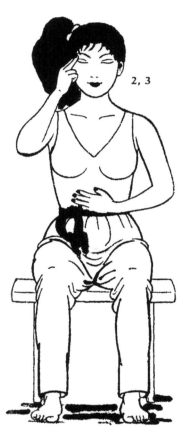

2, 3

- *Chu-in* is the pressure point midway between your navel and the pit of your stomach.

- *In-dou* is the pressure point between your eyebrows.

2. Place your left hand on your *chu-in* pressure point and place your right index finger on your *in-dou* pressure point.
3. Massage around your eyes, as illustrated. As you massage around the top of your eyes, inhale through your nose. As you massage around the bottom of your eyes, exhale through your mouth. Massage 10 to 20 times.
4. Cool down with *shu-kon*.

Cool down with *shu-kon*

1. *Ko-chi*: Make a chewing motion with your mouth five to 100 times.
2. *Tu-na*: Sit on a chair or sit cross-legged on the floor with your eyes closed. Calm your mind. Inhale through your nose and hold your breath for two seconds. While you are holding your breath, imagine that *chi* is flowing from your brain and down your spinal cord and lower back. Exhale slowly through your mouth. When you breathe out, imagine that you are releasing the old *chi* from your body. When you breathe in, imagine that you are inhaling fresh *chi* from nature.

3. *Su-wien*: Wipe the inside of your mouth with your tongue three times. Keeping your tongue behind your upper front teeth, inhale through your mouth. Close your lips and move the air around with your lips and cheeks as if you were cleaning your mouth with it. Do this five to 10 times. If saliva begins to collect in your mouth while you are doing this, swallow it.
4. *Shi-yen*: As you inhale, put your index fingers on the *in-dou* pressure point and massage along your eyebrows until you reach the *tai-you* pressure points. Continue massaging your face until you reach the *hin-sha* pressure points and then massage your neck and chest as shown in the illustration. Repeat three times.

For Tinnitus (Ringing or Whistling in the Ear): *Shi-a-min-gu*

1. In the cross-legged position, warm up with *chi-shi*.
2. Put your index fingers in your ears and twist them around three times, as if cleaning out the insides of your ears.

3. While breathing deeply, push your fingers as far into your ears as they can comfortably go. Take your fingers out of your ears and cover your ears with your hands.

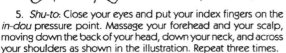

5. *Shu-to*: Close your eyes and put your index fingers on the *in-dou* pressure point. Massage your forehead and your scalp, moving down the back of your head, down your neck, and across your shoulders as shown in the illustration. Repeat three times.

6. *Shun-yo*: Sit on a chair and lift both of your arms up, back, and over your head with your wrists bent. Lift your feet off the floor and bend your toes. Inhale slowly and stretch your back. Then exhale while you bring your arms down to your sides and relax your entire body. Repeat twice.

4. Put your hands behind your head. Using your two middle fingers, tap your head six to 12 times with each hand.
5. Cool down with *shu-kon*.

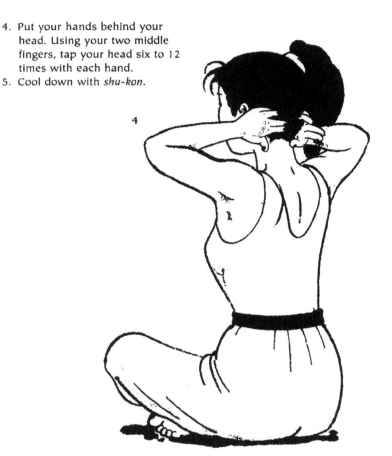

4

Warm up with *chi-shi*

1. *Be-mu*: Stand up, sit on a chair, or sit cross-legged on the floor with your eyes closed.
2. *Chang-tsuo*: Calm your mind.
3. *Tsuo-shou*: Put your palms together and rub them up and down until they feel warm.

4. *Bou-chee*: With your hands spread apart as if you were holding a big ball in front of you, inhale through your nose. Exhale through your mouth while bringing your hands back together.

Cool down with *shu-kon*

1. *Ko-chi*: Make a chewing motion with your mouth five to 100 times.
2. *Tu-na*: Sit on a chair or sit cross-legged on the floor with your eyes closed. Calm your mind. Inhale through your nose and hold your breath for two seconds. While you are holding your breath, imagine that *chi* is flowing from your brain and down your spinal cord and lower back. Exhale slowly through your mouth. When you breathe out, imagine that you are releasing the old *chi* from your body. When you breathe in, imagine that you are inhaling fresh *chi* from nature.

3. *Su-wien*: Wipe the inside of your mouth with your tongue three times. Keeping your tongue behind your upper front teeth, inhale through your mouth. Close your lips and move the air around with your lips and cheeks as if you were cleaning your mouth with it. Do this five to 10 times. If saliva begins to collect in your mouth while you are doing this, swallow it.
4. *Shi-yen*: As you inhale, put your index fingers on the *in-dou* pressure point and massage along your eyebrows until you reach the *tai-you* pressure points. Continue massaging your face until you reach the *hin-sha* pressure points and then massage your neck and chest as shown in the illustration. Repeat three times.

For Dry Mouth and Throat:
Shua-jao-shu-yen

1. In the cross-legged position, warm up with *chi-shi*.
2. Inhaling through your nose, make your hands into fists and bend them at the wrists. Raise your fists over your head. Exhaling, bring your hands down. Repeat three times.
3. Wash the inside of your mouth with your tongue three to 36 times.
4. Swallow your saliva.
5. Cool down with *shu-kon*.

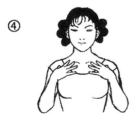

5. *Shu-to*: Close your eyes and put your index fingers on the *in-dou* pressure point. Massage your forehead and your scalp, moving down the back of your head, down your neck, and across your shoulders as shown in the illustration. Repeat three times.

6. *Shun-yo*: Sit on a chair and lift both of your arms up, back, and over your head with your wrists bent. Lift your feet off the floor and bend your toes. Inhale slowly and stretch your back. Then exhale while you bring your arms down to your sides and relax your entire body. Repeat twice.

For Difficulty in Swallowing Food: *Bai-shun-da-pwi*

1. In the standing position, warm up with *chi-shi*.
2. With your fingers spread apart, hit the right side of your chest with your left hand and then hit the left side of your chest with your right hand. Repeat six to 32 times.
3. Hit your left shoulder with your right hand and then hit your right shoulder with your left hand. Repeat six to 32 times.
4. Do the same thing on your back 32 times.
5. Cool down with *shu-kon*.

Warm up with *chi-shi*

1. *Be-mu*: Stand up, sit on a chair, or sit cross-legged on the floor with your eyes closed.
2. *Chang-tsuo*: Calm your mind.
3. *Tsuo-shou*: Put your palms together and rub them up and down until they feel warm.

4. *Bou-chee*: With your hands spread apart as if you were holding a big ball in front of you, inhale through your nose. Exhale through your mouth while bringing your hands back together.

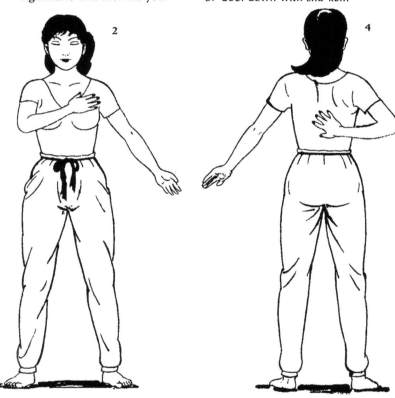

Cool down with *shu-kon*

1. *Ko-chi*: Make a chewing motion with your mouth five to 100 times.
2. *Tu-na*: Sit on a chair or sit cross-legged on the floor with your eyes closed. Calm your mind. Inhale through your nose and hold your breath for two seconds. While you are holding your breath, imagine that *chi* is flowing from your brain and down your spinal cord and lower back. Exhale slowly through your mouth. When you breathe out, imagine that you are releasing the old *chi* from your body. When you breathe in, imagine that you are inhaling fresh *chi* from nature.

3. *Su-wien*: Wipe the inside of your mouth with your tongue three times. Keeping your tongue behind your upper front teeth, inhale through your mouth. Close your lips and move the air around with your lips and cheeks as if you were cleaning your mouth with it. Do this five to 10 times. If saliva begins to collect in your mouth while you are doing this, swallow it.
4. *Shi-yen*: As you inhale, put your index fingers on the *in-dou* pressure point and massage along your eyebrows until you reach the *tai-you* pressure points. Continue massaging your face until you reach the *hin-sha* pressure points and then massage your neck and chest as shown in the illustration. Repeat three times.

For Runny Nose:
Shi-bi-ban-zo

1. In the cross-legged position, warm up with *chi-shi*.
2. Massage the sides of your nose with your index fingers, from the *in-dou* pressure point down to the *gei-kon* pressure points. Repeat 32 times.
3. Stretch your legs out in front of you and grab your toes. Breathe deeply three times.
4. Cool down with *shu-kon*.

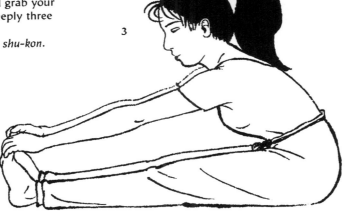

- *In-dou* is the pressure point between your eyebrows.
- *Gei-kon* are the pressure points on the outside of your nostrils.

5. *Shu-to*: Close your eyes and put your index fingers on the *in-dou* pressure point. Massage your forehead and your scalp, moving down the back of your head, down your neck, and across your shoulders as shown in the illustration. Repeat three times.

6. *Shun-yo*: Sit on a chair and lift both of your arms up, back, and over your head with your wrists bent. Lift your feet off the floor and bend your toes. Inhale slowly and stretch your back. Then exhale while you bring your arms down to your sides and relax your entire body. Repeat twice.

Specific Breathing Techniques to Prevent and Treat Nervous-System and Mental Disorders

Neuralgia

1. For Headache: *Shao-no-fon-wow*

1. In the cross-legged position, warm up with *chi-shi*.

2. Place your fingertips on the back of your neck, just under your head.

3. Massage your neck as if you were trying to dig out all the pain in your head. As you massage, inhale through your nose and exhale through your mouth.

4. Repeat six to 12 times.

5. Cool down with *shu-kon*.

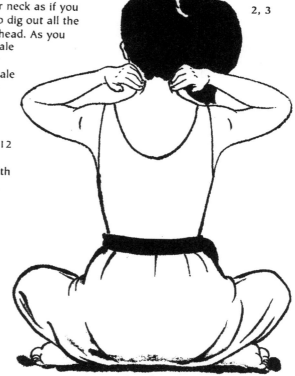

2, 3

Warm up with *chi-shi*

1. *Be-mu*: Stand up, sit on a chair, or sit cross-legged on the floor with your eyes closed.

2. *Chang-tsuo*: Calm your mind.

3. *Tsuo-shou*: Put your palms together and rub them up and down until they feel warm.

4. *Bou-chee*: With your hands spread apart as if you were holding a big ball in front of you, inhale through your nose. Exhale through your mouth while bringing your hands back together.

Cool down with *shu-kon*

1. *Ko-chi*: Make a chewing motion with your mouth five to 100 times.

2. *Tu-na*: Sit on a chair or sit cross-legged on the floor with your eyes closed. Calm your mind. Inhale through your nose and hold your breath for two seconds. While you are holding your breath, imagine that *chi* is flowing from your brain and down your spinal cord and lower back. Exhale slowly through your mouth. When you breathe out, imagine that you are releasing the old *chi* from your body. When you breathe in, imagine that you are inhaling fresh *chi* from nature.

3. *Su-wien*: Wipe the inside of your mouth with your tongue three times. Keeping your tongue behind your upper front teeth, inhale through your mouth. Close your lips and move the air around with your lips and cheeks as if you were cleaning your mouth with it. Do this five to 10 times. If saliva begins to collect in your mouth while you are doing this, swallow it.

4. *Shi-yen*: As you inhale, put your index fingers on the *in-dou* pressure point and massage along your eyebrows until you reach the *tai-you* pressure points. Continue massaging your face until you reach the *hin-sha* pressure points and then massage your neck and chest as shown in the illustration. Repeat three times.

2. For Facial Pain: *Fei-je-jan-yo*

1. In the standing position, warm up with *chi-shi.*
2. Form a T with your feet, turning your right foot out and positioning your left food perpendicular to it. Stand tall, but stay relaxed.
3. Extend the index and middle fingers of your right hand as if you were making them into the blade of a knife. Rest your left arm on your back and turn your head toward the left. Inhaling deeply through your nose, swing your right arm up over your head. Swing your right arm down as you exhale.
4. Switch arms and repeat step 3. Face right as you swing your left arm up and down. Repeat six to 12 times on each side.
5. Cool down with the *ko-chi, tu-na,* and *su-wien* steps of *shu-kon.*

1, 2

5. *Shu-to:* Close your eyes and put your index fingers on the *in-dou* pressure point. Massage your forehead and your scalp, moving down the back of your head, down your neck, and across your shoulders as shown in the illustration. Repeat three times.

6. *Shun-yo:* Sit on a chair and lift both of your arms up, back, and over your head with your wrists bent. Lift your feet off the floor and bend your toes. Inhale slowly and stretch your back. Then exhale while you bring your arms down to your sides and relax your entire body. Repeat twice.

3. For Sciatica: *Kao-gowae-twuo-tei*

1. In the standing position, warm up with *chi-shi*. Using a stick (a cane or umbrella, for example), stand with your legs apart. Close your eyes and relax your body. Calm your mind.

2. Lean back, letting your weight rest on the stick—first on the left side of your back muscle and then on the right side. Repeat six to 24 times.

2

Warm up with *chi-shi*

1. *Be-mu*: Stand up, sit on a chair, or sit cross-legged on the floor with your eyes closed.
2. *Chang-tsuo*: Calm your mind.
3. *Tsuo-shou*: Put your palms together and rub them up and down until they feel warm.

4. *Bou-chee*: With your hands spread apart as if you were holding a big ball in front of you, inhale through your nose. Exhale through your mouth while bringing your hands back together.

Cool down with *shu-kon*

1. *Ko-chi*: Make a chewing motion with your mouth five to 100 times.
2. *Tu-na*: Sit on a chair or sit cross-legged on the floor with your eyes closed. Calm your mind. Inhale through your nose and hold your breath for two seconds. While you are holding your breath, imagine that *chi* is flowing from your brain and down your spinal cord and lower back. Exhale slowly through your mouth. When you breathe out, imagine that you are releasing the old *chi* from your body. When you breathe in, imagine that you are inhaling fresh *chi* from nature.

3. *Su-wien*: Wipe the inside of your mouth with your tongue three times. Keeping your tongue behind your upper front teeth, inhale through your mouth. Close your lips and move the air around with your lips and cheeks as if you were cleaning your mouth with it. Do this five to 10 times. If saliva begins to collect in your mouth while you are doing this, swallow it.
4. *Shi-yen*: As you inhale, put your index fingers on the *in-dou* pressure point and massage along your eyebrows until you reach the *tai-you* pressure points. Continue massaging your face until you reach the *hin-sha* pressure points and then massage your neck and chest as shown in the illustration. Repeat three times.

3

3. Crouch down on the floor and
stretch your back. Breathing
deeply, hold the stick with both
hands and swing it back and
forth on the ground, from left to
right. Repeat 18 times.
4. Cool down with *shu-kon*.

4. For Sciatica in the Legs: *Ban-chan-to-shue*

2, 3

1. In the standing position, warm
up with *chi-shi*.
2. Put your right hand on the wall
and your left hand on your hip
as illustrated.
3. Lift your right knee. Keeping
your right foot bent at a 90-
degree angle, try to straighten
your leg. Repeat six to 24 times.
4. Switch sides, putting your left
hand on the wall and your right
hand on your hip, and do the
same thing with your left leg.
5. Cool down with *shu-kon*.

5. *Shu-to*: Close your eyes and put your index fingers on the
in-dou pressure point. Massage your forehead and your scalp,
moving down the back of your head, down your neck, and across
your shoulders as shown in the illustration. Repeat three times.

6. *Shun-yo*: Sit on a chair and lift both of your arms up, back,
and over your head with your wrists bent. Lift your feet off the
floor and bend your toes. Inhale slowly and stretch your back.
Then exhale while you bring your arms down to your sides and
relax your entire body. Repeat twice.

Insomnia

1. For Sleeplessness: *Ko-chi*

Do the *ko-chi* step of *shu-kon*, making a chewing motion with your mouth 12 to 24 times.

Warm up with *chi-shi*

1. *Be-mu*: Stand up, sit on a chair, or sit cross-legged on the floor with your eyes closed.
2. *Chang-tsuo*: Calm your mind.
3. *Tsuo-shou*: Put your palms together and rub them up and down until they feel warm.

4. *Bou-chee*: With your hands spread apart as if you were holding a big ball in front of you, inhale through your nose. Exhale through your mouth while bringing your hands back together.

2. For Fatigue: *Pei-ta-chuen-shen*

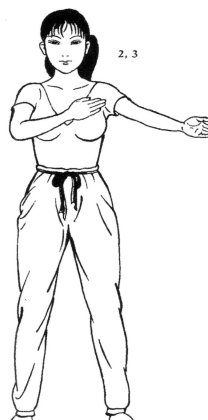

2, 3

1. Standing with your legs slightly apart, warm up with *chi-shi*.
2. Holding your arms as illustrated, use the palm of your right hand to hit the left side of your chest and your left shoulder. Continue down your left arm, hitting your forearm and wrist. Then come back up, hitting your left forearm, shoulder, and chest.
3. Reverse the procedure, using the palm of your left hand to hit the right side of your chest, your right shoulder, and your right arm.
4. Using both hands, move down your entire body, hitting the front of your chest, your stomach, the insides of your legs, and your ankles. Then come back up the outsides of your legs.
5. Repeat steps 2 through 4 twice.
6. Cool down with *shu-kon*.

Cool down with *shu-kon*

1. *Ko-chi*: Make a chewing motion with your mouth five to 100 times.
2. *Tu-na*: Sit on a chair or sit cross-legged on the floor with your eyes closed. Calm your mind. Inhale through your nose and hold your breath for two seconds. While you are holding your breath, imagine that *chi* is flowing from your brain and down your spinal cord and lower back. Exhale slowly through your mouth. When you breathe out, imagine that you are releasing the old *chi* from your body. When you breathe in, imagine that you are inhaling fresh *chi* from nature.

3. *Su-wien*: Wipe the inside of your mouth with your tongue three times. Keeping your tongue behind your upper front teeth, inhale through your mouth. Close your lips and move the air around with your lips and cheeks as if you were cleaning your mouth with it. Do this five to 10 times. If saliva begins to collect in your mouth while you are doing this, swallow it.
4. *Shi-yen*: As you inhale, put your index fingers on the *in-dou* pressure point and massage along your eyebrows until you reach the *tai-you* pressure points. Continue massaging your face until you reach the *hin-sha* pressure points and then massage your neck and chest as shown in the illustration. Repeat three times.

To Prevent Grinding of the Teeth:
Shi-a-min-gu

1. In the cross-legged position, warm up with *chi-shi*.
2. Put your index fingers in your ears and twist them around three times as if cleaning out the insides of your ears.

3. While breathing deeply, push your fingers as far into your ears as they can comfortably go. Take your fingers out of your ears and cover your ears with your hands.

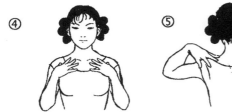

5. *Shu-to*: Close your eyes and put your index fingers on the *in-dou* pressure point. Massage your forehead and your scalp, moving down the back of your head, down your neck, and across your shoulders as shown in the illustration. Repeat three times.

6. *Shun-yo*: Sit on a chair and lift both of your arms up, back, and over your head with your wrists bent. Lift your feet off the floor and bend your toes. Inhale slowly and stretch your back. Then exhale while you bring your arms down to your sides and relax your entire body. Repeat twice.

4. Put your hands behind your head. Using your two middle fingers, tap your head six to 12 times with each hand.
5. Cool down with *shu-kon*.

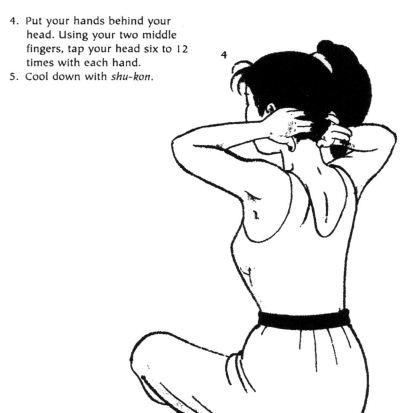

Warm up with *chi-shi*

1. *Be-mu*: Stand up, sit on a chair, or sit cross-legged on the floor with your eyes closed.
2. *Chang-tsuo*: Calm your mind.
3. *Tsuo-shou*: Put your palms together and rub them up and down until they feel warm.

4. *Bou-chee*: With your hands spread apart as if you were holding a big ball in front of you, inhale through your nose. Exhale through your mouth while bringing your hands back together.

Cool down with *shu-kon*

1. *Ko-chi*: Make a chewing motion with your mouth five to 100 times.
2. *Tu-na*: Sit on a chair or sit cross-legged on the floor with your eyes closed. Calm your mind. Inhale through your nose and hold your breath for two seconds. While you are holding your breath, imagine that *chi* is flowing from your brain and down your spinal cord and lower back. Exhale slowly through your mouth. When you breathe out, imagine that you are releasing the old *chi* from your body. When you breathe in, imagine that you are inhaling fresh *chi* from nature.

3. *Su-wien*: Wipe the inside of your mouth with your tongue three times. Keeping your tongue behind your upper front teeth, inhale through your mouth. Close your lips and move the air around with your lips and cheeks as if you were cleaning your mouth with it. Do this five to 10 times. If saliva begins to collect in your mouth while you are doing this, swallow it.
4. *Shi-yen*: As you inhale, put your index fingers on the *in-dou* pressure point and massage along your eyebrows until you reach the *tai-you* pressure points. Continue massaging your face until you reach the *hin-sha* pressure points and then massage your neck and chest as shown in the illustration. Repeat three times.

Partial Paralysis

1. For Mild Paralysis: *Go-wae-shen-zu-ru*

1. In the standing position, warm up with *chi-shi*.
2. Holding a stick between your thighs, put your weight on your right leg. With your index and middle fingers together, point your right hand forward and up and point your left hand backward and down. Turn your head to the left.
3. Switch sides and do the same thing.
4. Repeat 12 to 24 times steps 2 and 3.
5. Cool down with *shu-kon*.

5. *Shu-to*: Close your eyes and put your index fingers on the *in-dou* pressure point. Massage your forehead and your scalp, moving down the back of your head, down your neck, and across your shoulders as shown in the illustration. Repeat three times.

6. *Shun-yo*: Sit on a chair and lift both of your arms up, back, and over your head with your wrists bent. Lift your feet off the floor and bend your toes. Inhale slowly and stretch your back. Then exhale while you bring your arms down to your sides and relax your entire body. Repeat twice.

2. For Severe Paralysis on One Side of the Body: *Zu-yan-po-fon*

Note: The following instructions are written for paralysis on the right side of the body. If your paralysis is on the left side, do the exercise on your left side.

Warm up with *chi–shi*

1. *Be-mu*: Stand up, sit on a chair, or sit cross-legged on the floor with your eyes closed.
2. *Chang-tsuo*: Calm your mind.
3. *Tsuo-shou*: Put your palms together and rub them up and down until they feel warm.

4. *Bou-chee*: With your hands spread apart as if you were holding a big ball in front of you, inhale through your nose. Exhale through your mouth while bringing your hands back together.

1. In the cross-legged position, warm up with *chi-shi*.
2. Place your right hand on the right side of your stomach and place your left hand on your knee.
3. Inhaling *chi* through your nose, imagine that you are guiding it through the right side of your brain and body and out through your *yu-sen* pressure point, as illustrated.

2, 3

Cool down with *shu-kon*

1. *Ko-chi*: Make a chewing motion with your mouth five to 100 times.
2. *Tu-na*: Sit on a chair or sit cross-legged on the floor with your eyes closed. Calm your mind. Inhale through your nose and hold your breath for two seconds. While you are holding your breath, imagine that *chi* is flowing from your brain and down your spinal cord and lower back. Exhale slowly through your mouth. When you breathe out, imagine that you are releasing the old *chi* from your body. When you breathe in, imagine that you are inhaling fresh *chi* from nature.

3. *Su-wien*: Wipe the inside of your mouth with your tongue three times. Keeping your tongue behind your upper front teeth, inhale through your mouth. Close your lips and move the air around with your lips and cheeks as if you were cleaning your mouth with it. Do this five to 10 times. If saliva begins to collect in your mouth while you are doing this, swallow it.
4. *Shi-yen*: As you inhale, put your index fingers on the *in-dou* pressure point and massage along your eyebrows until you reach the *tai-you* pressure points. Continue massaging your face until you reach the *hin-sha* pressure points and then massage your neck and chest as shown in the illustration. Repeat three times.

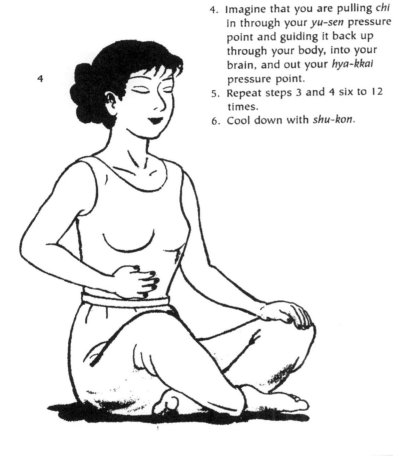

4

4. Imagine that you are pulling *chi* in through your *yu-sen* pressure point and guiding it back up through your body, into your brain, and out your *hya-kkai* pressure point.
5. Repeat steps 3 and 4 six to 12 times.
6. Cool down with *shu-kon*.

• *Yu-sen* is the pressure point a little above the center of the sole of your foot. If you bend your toes, you will see the hollow that forms around it.

• *Hya-kkai* is the pressure point located on top of your head, midway between your two earlobes.

5. *Shu-to*: Close your eyes and put your index fingers on the *in-dou* pressure point. Massage your forehead and your scalp, moving down the back of your head, down your neck, and across your shoulders as shown in the illustration. Repeat three times.

6. *Shun-yo*: Sit on a chair and lift both of your arms up, back, and over your head with your wrists bent. Lift your feet off the floor and bend your toes. Inhale slowly and stretch your back. Then exhale while you bring your arms down to your sides and relax your entire body. Repeat twice.

For Dizziness and Fainting: *Ryam-shao-bao-din*

1. In the sitting position, warm up with *chi-shi*.

2. Without using your thumbs, put your hands on your head, with your index fingers positioned on your *hya-kkai* pressure point.

3. Inhaling through your nose, imagine that you are drawing *chi* in through your head. Exhaling through your nose, imagine that you are guiding the *chi* down to your *shimotanden* pressure point. Repeat 10 to 20 times.

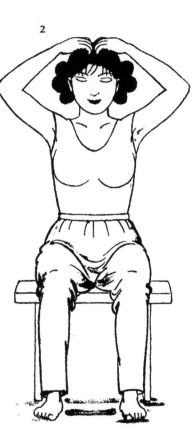

Warm up with *chi-shi*

1. *Be-mu*: Stand up, sit on a chair, or sit cross-legged on the floor with your eyes closed.

2. *Chang-tsuo*: Calm your mind.

3. *Tsuo-shou*: Put your palms together and rub them up and down until they feel warm.

4. *Bou-chee*: With your hands spread apart as if you were holding a big ball in front of you, inhale through your nose. Exhale through your mouth while bringing your hands back together.

- *Hya-kkai* is the pressure point located on top of your head, midway between your two earlobes.

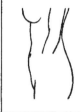

- *Shimotanden* is the pressure point approximately 3 inches below your navel.

Cool down with *shu-kon*

1. *Ko-chi*: Make a chewing motion with your mouth five to 100 times.

2. *Tu-na*: Sit on a chair or sit cross-legged on the floor with your eyes closed. Calm your mind. Inhale through your nose and hold your breath for two seconds. While you are holding your breath, imagine that *chi* is flowing from your brain and down your spinal cord and lower back. Exhale slowly through your mouth. When you breathe out, imagine that you are releasing the old *chi* from your body. When you breathe in, imagine that you are inhaling fresh *chi* from nature.

3. *Su-wien*: Wipe the inside of your mouth with your tongue three times. Keeping your tongue behind your upper front teeth, inhale through your mouth. Close your lips and move the air around with your lips and cheeks as if you were cleaning your mouth with it. Do this five to 10 times. If saliva begins to collect in your mouth while you are doing this, swallow it.

4. *Shi-yen*: As you inhale, put your index fingers on the *in-dou* pressure point and massage along your eyebrows until you reach the *tai-you* pressure points. Continue massaging your face until you reach the *hin-sha* pressure points and then massage your neck and chest as shown in the illustration. Repeat three times.

Epilepsy

1. For Severe Epilepsy: *Shen-zu-an-chi*

1. In the cross-legged position, warm up with *chi-shi*.
2. Extend your legs in front of you.
3. Massage your legs with both hands. Inhale deeply as you massage down from your knees to your toes. Exhale deeply as you massage back up from your toes to your knees. Repeat 12 to 24 times. Cool down with *shu-kon*.

2, 3

5. *Shu-to*: Close your eyes and put your index fingers on the *in-dou* pressure point. Massage your forehead and your scalp, moving down the back of your head, down your neck, and across your shoulders as shown in the illustration. Repeat three times.

6. *Shun-yo*: Sit on a chair and lift both of your arms up, back, and over your head with your wrists bent. Lift your feet off the floor and bend your toes. Inhale slowly and stretch your back. Then exhale while you bring your arms down to your sides and relax your entire body. Repeat twice.

2. For Mild Epilepsy: *Tui-chowan-wan-yue*

1. In the standing position, warm up with *chi-shi*.

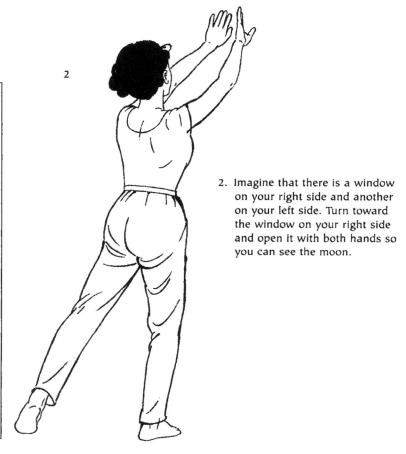

2

Warm up with *chi-shi*

1. *Be-mu*: Stand up, sit on a chair, or sit cross-legged on the floor with your eyes closed.
2. *Chang-tsuo*: Calm your mind.
3. *Tsuo-shou*: Put your palms together and rub them up and down until they feel warm.

4. *Bou-chee*: With your hands spread apart as if you were holding a big ball in front of you, inhale through your nose. Exhale through your mouth while bringing your hands back together.

2. Imagine that there is a window on your right side and another on your left side. Turn toward the window on your right side and open it with both hands so you can see the moon.

Cool down with *shu-kon*

1. *Ko-chi*: Make a chewing motion with your mouth five to 100 times.
2. *Tu-na*: Sit on a chair or sit cross-legged on the floor with your eyes closed. Calm your mind. Inhale through your nose and hold your breath for two seconds. While you are holding your breath, imagine that *chi* is flowing from your brain and down your spinal cord and lower back. Exhale slowly through your mouth. When you breathe out, imagine that you are releasing the old *chi* from your body. When you breathe in, imagine that you are inhaling fresh *chi* from nature.

3. *Su-wien*: Wipe the inside of your mouth with your tongue three times. Keeping your tongue behind your upper front teeth, inhale through your mouth. Close your lips and move the air around with your lips and cheeks as if you were cleaning your mouth with it. Do this five to 10 times. If saliva begins to collect in your mouth while you are doing this, swallow it.
4. *Shi-yen*: As you inhale, put your index fingers on the *in-dou* pressure point and massage along your eyebrows until you reach the *tai-you* pressure points. Continue massaging your face until you reach the *hin-sha* pressure points and then massage your neck and chest as shown in the illustration. Repeat three times.

3. Bring your hands back behind you. Turn and open the window on your left side to see the moon and then bring your hands back behind you.
4. Repeat steps 2 and 3 three to 12 times. Hit your lower back with both hands.
5. Cool down with *shu-kon*.

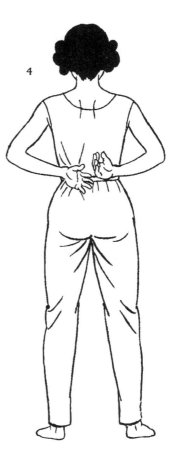

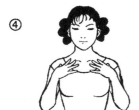

5. *Shu-to*: Close your eyes and put your index fingers on the *in-dou* pressure point. Massage your forehead and your scalp, moving down the back of your head, down your neck, and across your shoulders as shown in the illustration. Repeat three times.

6. *Shun-yo*: Sit on a chair and lift both of your arms up, back, and over your head with your wrists bent. Lift your feet off the floor and bend your toes. Inhale slowly and stretch your back. Then exhale while you bring your arms down to your sides and relax your entire body. Repeat twice.

Specific Breathing Techniques to Prevent and Treat Cancer

Prevention and Treatment

1. For Cancer in the Chest: *Ton-ren-mai-zan*

1. In the cross-legged position, warm up with *chi-shi*.

2. Massage your neck with your fingers.
3. While inhaling deeply through your nose, press your *dan-chu* pressure point with your right index finger and press your *hya-kkai* pressure point with your left index finger.
3. Exhale through your mouth and switch hands. Inhale deeply and switch hands.
4. Repeat steps 2 and 3 nine times.
5. Cool down with *shu-kon*.

Warm up with *chi-shi*

1. *Be-mu*: Stand up, sit on a chair, or sit cross-legged on the floor with your eyes closed.
2. *Chang-tsuo*: Calm your mind.
3. *Tsuo-shou*: Put your palms together and rub them up and down until they feel warm.

4. *Bou-chee*: With your hands spread apart as if you were holding a big ball in front of you, inhale through your nose. Exhale through your mouth while bringing your hands back together.

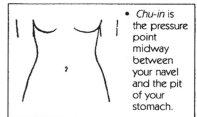

- *Hya-kkai* is the pressure point located on top of your head, midway between your two earlobes.

- *Chu-in* is the pressure point midway between your navel and the pit of your stomach.

Cool down with *shu-kon*

1. *Ko-chi*: Make a chewing motion with your mouth five to 100 times.
2. *Tu-na*: Sit on a chair or sit cross-legged on the floor with your eyes closed. Calm your mind. Inhale through your nose and hold your breath for two seconds. While you are holding your breath, imagine that *chi* is flowing from your brain and down your spinal cord and lower back. Exhale slowly through your mouth. When you breathe out, imagine that you are releasing the old *chi* from your body. When you breathe in, imagine that you are inhaling fresh *chi* from nature.

3. *Su-wien*: Wipe the inside of your mouth with your tongue three times. Keeping your tongue behind your upper front teeth, inhale through your mouth. Close your lips and move the air around with your lips and cheeks as if you were cleaning your mouth with it. Do this five to 10 times. If saliva begins to collect in your mouth while you are doing this, swallow it.
4. *Shi-yen*: As you inhale, put your index fingers on the *in-dou* pressure point and massage along your eyebrows until you reach the *tai-you* pressure points. Continue massaging your face until you reach the *hin-sha* pressure points and then massage your neck and chest as shown in the illustration. Repeat three times.

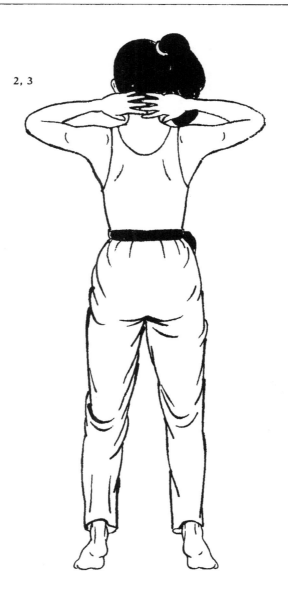

2, 3

2. For Fatigue: *Bo-to-din-zu*

1. In the standing position, warm up with *chi-shi*.
2. Put your hands on the back of your neck as illustrated and stand on your toes with your legs apart.
3. Lift yourself up and down on your toes without letting your heels touch the ground. As you lift yourself up, imagine that you are lifting your stomach and rectum. Repeat six to 12 times.
4. Cool down with the *shi-yen* and *shun-yo* steps of *shou-kon*.

5. *Shu-to*: Close your eyes and put your index fingers on the *in-dou* pressure point. Massage your forehead and your scalp, moving down the back of your head, down your neck, and across your shoulders as shown in the illustration. Repeat three times.

6. *Shun-yo*: Sit on a chair and lift both of your arms up, back, and over your head with your wrists bent. Lift your feet off the floor and bend your toes. Inhale slowly and stretch your back. Then exhale while you bring your arms down to your sides and relax your entire body. Repeat twice.

After Chemotherapy

1. For Hedrocele or Oneirogmus: *Jo-tie-nho-hao*

1. In the cross-legged position, warm up with *chi-shi*.

2. Pull up on the sides of your stomach with your hands. As you inhale, imagine that you are also pulling up your groin.

3. Exhale and relax your hands and body.
4. Repeat 12 to 24 times steps 2 and 3.
5. Cool down with *shu-kon*.

2

Warm up with *chi-shi*

1. *Be-mu*: Stand up, sit on a chair, or sit cross-legged on the floor with your eyes closed.
2. *Chang-tsuo*: Calm your mind.
3. *Tsuo-shou*: Put your palms together and rub them up and down until they feel warm.

4. *Bou-chee*: With your hands spread apart as if you were holding a big ball in front of you, inhale through your nose. Exhale through your mouth while bringing your hands back together.

Cool down with *shu-kon*

1. *Ko-chi*: Make a chewing motion with your mouth five to 100 times.
2. *Tu-na*: Sit on a chair or sit cross-legged on the floor with your eyes closed. Calm your mind. Inhale through your nose and hold your breath for two seconds. While you are holding your breath, imagine that *chi* is flowing from your brain and down your spinal cord and lower back. Exhale slowly through your mouth. When you breathe out, imagine that you are releasing the old *chi* from your body. When you breathe in, imagine that you are inhaling fresh *chi* from nature.

3. *Su-wien*: Wipe the inside of your mouth with your tongue three times. Keeping your tongue behind your upper front teeth, inhale through your mouth. Close your lips and move the air around with your lips and cheeks as if you were cleaning your mouth with it. Do this five to 10 times. If saliva begins to collect in your mouth while you are doing this, swallow it.
4. *Shi-yen*: As you inhale, put your index fingers on the *in-dou* pressure point and massage along your eyebrows until you reach the *tai-you* pressure points. Continue massaging your face until you reach the *hin-sha* pressure points and then massage your neck and chest as shown in the illustration. Repeat three times.

2. For Anxiety or Nervousness Associated With Chemotherapy: *Rin-niu-shin-bin*

1. In the standing position, warm up with *chi-shi*.
2. As you inhale through your nose, take one step forward with your right foot. At the same time, lift your right arm with your palm facing up and your thumb extended. Press the *nai-kan* pressure point on your right arm with your left thumb as illustrated.
3. As you exhale through your nose, switch your arms and legs and repeat step 2. Repeat 10 to 24 times on each side.
4. Cool down with *shu-kon*.

• *Nai-kan* is the pressure point located on the inside of your arm, approximately one inch above your wrist.

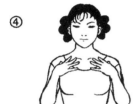

5. *Shu-to*: Close your eyes and put your index fingers on the *in-dou* pressure point. Massage your forehead and your scalp, moving down the back of your head, down your neck, and across your shoulders as shown in the illustration. Repeat three times.

6. *Shun-yo*: Sit on a chair and lift both of your arms up, back, and over your head with your wrists bent. Lift your feet off the floor and bend your toes. Inhale slowly and stretch your back. Then exhale while you bring your arms down to your sides and relax your entire body. Repeat twice.

3. For Excessive Bleeding: *Tai-shi-yan-jan*

1. In a very quiet room, warm up with *chi-shi* while lying on your back.
2. Close your eyes. Very, very calmly inhale through your nose and exhale through your mouth.
3. Repeat step 2 about 300 times. We call this the "breathing technique for a sleeping baby" because it is so peaceful and quiet.
4. Cool down with *shu-kon*.

Warm up with *chi-shi*

1. *Be-mu*: Stand up, sit on a chair, or sit cross-legged on the floor with your eyes closed.
2. *Chang-tsuo*: Calm your mind.
3. *Tsuo-shou*: Put your palms together and rub them up and down until they feel warm.

4. *Bou-chee*: With your hands spread apart as if you were holding a big ball in front of you, inhale through your nose. Exhale through your mouth while bringing your hands back together.

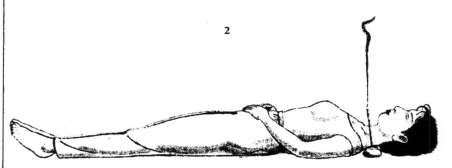

2

Cool down with *shu-kon*

1. *Ko-chi*: Make a chewing motion with your mouth five to 100 times.
2. *Tu-na*: Sit on a chair or sit cross-legged on the floor with your eyes closed. Calm your mind. Inhale through your nose and hold your breath for two seconds. While you are holding your breath, imagine that *chi* is flowing from your brain and down your spinal cord and lower back. Exhale slowly through your mouth. When you breathe out, imagine that you are releasing the old *chi* from your body. When you breathe in, imagine that you are inhaling fresh *chi* from nature.

3. *Su-wien*: Wipe the inside of your mouth with your tongue three times. Keeping your tongue behind your upper front teeth, inhale through your mouth. Close your lips and move the air around with your lips and cheeks as if you were cleaning your mouth with it. Do this five to 10 times. If saliva begins to collect in your mouth while you are doing this, swallow it.
4. *Shi-yen*: As you inhale, put your index fingers on the *in-dou* pressure point and massage along your eyebrows until you reach the *tai-you* pressure points. Continue massaging your face until you reach the *hin-sha* pressure points and then massage your neck and chest as shown in the illustration. Repeat three times.

After Surgery

1. For Anxiety or Chest Pain: *An-chi-ti-chi*

1, 2

1. After warming up with *chi-shi*, form a T with your feet, turning your right foot out and positioning your left food perpendicular to it. Stand tall, but stay relaxed.
2. Imagine that you are holding a sword in your right hand. Place your left hand on the end of the sword.
3. Look at your left hand and breathe deeply.
4. Switch hands and breathe deeply again.
5. Repeat steps 3 and 4 six to 12 times.
6. Cool down with *shu-kon*.

④

⑤

⑥

5. *Shu-to*: Close your eyes and put your index fingers on the *in-dou* pressure point. Massage your forehead and your scalp, moving down the back of your head, down your neck, and across your shoulders as shown in the illustration. Repeat three times.

6. *Shun-yo*: Sit on a chair and lift both of your arms up, back, and over your head with your wrists bent. Lift your feet off the floor and bend your toes. Inhale slowly and stretch your back. Then exhale while you bring your arms down to your sides and relax your entire body. Repeat twice.

2. To Ease Stiffness in the Neck and Shoulders Caused by Stress: *Fun-howan-jan-chi*

1. In the standing position, warm up with *chi-shi*.

Warm up with *chi-shi*

1. *Be-mu*: Stand up, sit on a chair, or sit cross-legged on the floor with your eyes closed.
2. *Chang-tsuo*: Calm your mind.
3. *Tsuo-shou*: Put your palms together and rub them up and down until they feel warm.

4. *Bou-chee*: With your hands spread apart as if you were holding a big ball in front of you, inhale through your nose. Exhale through your mouth while bringing your hands back together.

2. With your right hand on your stomach, slightly bend your lower back and knees and bring your left palm up as illustrated. As you do this, imagine that you are reaching up to the sky.

3. Switch hands and do the same thing. Repeat six to 24 times on each side.
4. Cool down with *shu-kon*.

Cool down with *shu-kon*

1. *Ko-chi*: Make a chewing motion with your mouth five to 100 times.
2. *Tu-na*: Sit on a chair or sit cross-legged on the floor with your eyes closed. Calm your mind. Inhale through your nose and hold your breath for two seconds. While you are holding your breath, imagine that *chi* is flowing from your brain and down your spinal cord and lower back. Exhale slowly through your mouth. When you breathe out, imagine that you are releasing the old *chi* from your body. When you breathe in, imagine that you are inhaling fresh *chi* from nature.

3. *Su-wien*: Wipe the inside of your mouth with your tongue three times. Keeping your tongue behind your upper front teeth, inhale through your mouth. Close your lips and move the air around with your lips and cheeks as if you were cleaning your mouth with it. Do this five to 10 times. If saliva begins to collect in your mouth while you are doing this, swallow it.
4. *Shi-yen*: As you inhale, put your index fingers on the *in-dou* pressure point and massage along your eyebrows until you reach the *tai-you* pressure points. Continue massaging your face until you reach the *hin-sha* pressure points and then massage your neck and chest as shown in the illustration. Repeat three times.

3. For Amnesia:
Ban-yun-shi-jin

1. In the cross-legged position, warm up with *chi-shi*.
2. Extend your legs in front of you and relax.
3. Grasp your toes and inhale through your nose. While pulling your toes up and toward your chest with your hands, try to push them down and away from your body as illustrated.
4. Exhale through your mouth and relax.
5. Repeat steps 3 and 4 six to 12 times.
6. Cool down with *shu-kon*.

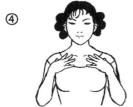

5. *Shu-to*: Close your eyes and put your index fingers on the *in-dou* pressure point. Massage your forehead and your scalp, moving down the back of your head, down your neck, and across your shoulders as shown in the illustration. Repeat three times.

6. *Shun-yo*: Sit on a chair and lift both of your arms up, back, and over your head with your wrists bent. Lift your feet off the floor and bend your toes. Inhale slowly and stretch your back. Then exhale while you bring your arms down to your sides and relax your entire body. Repeat twice.

4. For Fatigue: *Pei-ta-chuen-shen*

1. Standing with your legs slightly apart, warm up with *chi-shi*.

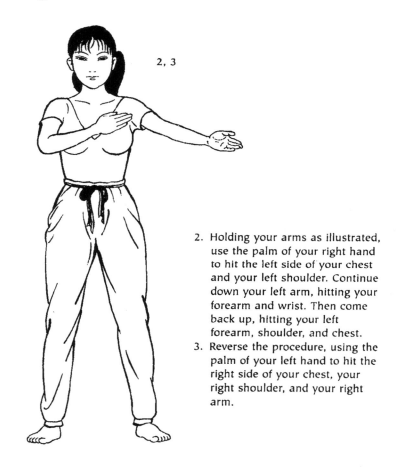

2, 3

Warm up with *chi-shi*

1. *Be-mu*: Stand up, sit on a chair, or sit cross-legged on the floor with your eyes closed.
2. *Chang-tsuo*: Calm your mind.
3. *Tsuo-shou*: Put your palms together and rub them up and down until they feel warm.

4. *Bou-chee*: With your hands spread apart as if you were holding a big ball in front of you, inhale through your nose. Exhale through your mouth while bringing your hands back together.

2. Holding your arms as illustrated, use the palm of your right hand to hit the left side of your chest and your left shoulder. Continue down your left arm, hitting your forearm and wrist. Then come back up, hitting your left forearm, shoulder, and chest.
3. Reverse the procedure, using the palm of your left hand to hit the right side of your chest, your right shoulder, and your right arm.

Cool down with *shu-kon*

1. *Ko-chi*: Make a chewing motion with your mouth five to 100 times.
2. *Tu-na*: Sit on a chair or sit cross-legged on the floor with your eyes closed. Calm your mind. Inhale through your nose and hold your breath for two seconds. While you are holding your breath, imagine that *chi* is flowing from your brain and down your spinal cord and lower back. Exhale slowly through your mouth. When you breathe out, imagine that you are releasing the old *chi* from your body. When you breathe in, imagine that you are inhaling fresh *chi* from nature.

3. *Su-wien*: Wipe the inside of your mouth with your tongue three times. Keeping your tongue behind your upper front teeth, inhale through your mouth. Close your lips and move the air around with your lips and cheeks as if you were cleaning your mouth with it. Do this five to 10 times. If saliva begins to collect in your mouth while you are doing this, swallow it.
4. *Shi-yen*: As you inhale, put your index fingers on the *in-dou* pressure point and massage along your eyebrows until you reach the *tai-you* pressure points. Continue massaging your face until you reach the *hin-sha* pressure points and then massage your neck and chest as shown in the illustration. Repeat three times.